BASIC
READING POWER 1
TEST BOOKLET

Linda Jeffries

Beatrice S. Mikulecky

PEARSON
Longman

Basic Reading Power 1 Test Booklet

Pearson Education, 10 Bank Street, White Plains, NY 10606

Staff credits: The people who made up the *Basic Reading Power 1 Test Booklet* team, representing editorial,
production, design, and manufacturing, are Pietro Alongi, Dave Dickey, Shelley Gazes, Massimo Rubini,
Jennifer Stem, and Ruth Voetmann.

Text design and composition: Rainbow Graphics
Text font: Times Roman

ISBN-13: 978-0-13-208534-2
ISBN-10: 0-13-208534-8

PEARSON LONGMAN ON THE WEB

Pearsonlongman.com offers online
resources for teachers and students. Access our
Companion Websites, our online catalog, and
our local offices around the world.

Visit us at **www.pearsonlongman.com**.

Printed in the United States of America

1 2 3 4 5 6 7 8 9 10—V0LA—14 13 12 11 10

CONTENTS

INTRODUCTION

This *Test Booklet* follows the format of the third edition of *Basic Reading Power 1*. It includes tests for Parts 2, 3, and 4. There are no tests for Part 1 because this part of the book deals with extensive reading, which is best evaluated with methods other than formal testing. (These are discussed in the *Teacher's Guide,* pages 7–9).

The introduction to each part of the test booklet includes a list of the tests in that part. This list also provides the following information about the tests:

1. The corresponding exercise(s) in the student book

The tests are intended to follow work that students do in the student book. Teachers can give a test when students have completed the exercise or exercises in the student book that present a given skill, strategy, or vocabulary set. Teachers should not give a test before students have completed the corresponding exercise or exercises.

2. The type of test: S = skill/strategy, V = vocabulary

S = Skills/Strategies Tests

The tests of skills and strategies reflect the approach taken in *Basic Reading Power 1*, where reading is viewed as a process involving many skills and strategies, including those involved in learning vocabulary. (This approach is explained in detail in the *Teacher's Guide.*) The teacher's goal in testing students on their mastery of a skill or strategy should be to verify how well students have understood the processes and if they can put the skill or strategy to use in their reading or learning. Research has shown this can best be measured by a test that reflects the format of the training. Therefore, the tests of this type are similar to the corresponding exercises in the student book.

In scoring tests of skills or strategies, teachers should keep in mind the aim of these tests and not simply look for the "correct" answer. In fact, for many exercises, the responses given in the Answer Key should be considered those that are most likely, but not necessarily the only ones. Teachers should accept answers that differ from those in the Answer Key if the students can justify them.

The tests of skills and strategies can also serve another purpose: further practice. According to the context and the level of the class, some teachers may find that their students (or some of them) need additional work in certain areas. This is the reason why two tests are sometimes included for some skills or strategies.

V = Vocabulary Tests

These tests aim to assess students' knowledge of the words and phrases targeted in *Basic Reading Power 1* in some units of Part 2 and in the Focus on Vocabulary sections of each of the units of Part 3.

UNIT TESTS

Part 1: Extensive Reading

As stated in the introduction to the test booklet, students should NOT be tested in a formal way on their extensive reading. Testing of comprehension or vocabulary would change the reading experience and could destroy their enjoyment of a story or book.

However, it is important for teachers to evaluate students' progress in extensive reading. There are several reasons for this. First, teachers may need some measure of students' work in this part of the course. Second, evaluating their reading will reinforce the idea that students should take extensive reading seriously. And third, some of the methods for evaluation also allow students to communicate their experiences and share them with others.

Teachers should first of all make it clear to students that they will be expected to fulfill the basic aim of extensive reading—to read a lot. There are several ways to do this. The teacher can establish a required number of books for all students. Alternatively, to increase student involvement and motivation, teachers can talk with students as a class about how many books they think they can read in a semester, and then ask each student to write a target number in his or her student book (for example, on page 53 beside the heading "Reading List"). During the semester, teachers should check students' progress toward their targets.

Teachers then need to assess how much students actually read and how well they understood what they read. This can be done using the various activities for talking or writing about books that are discussed in the *Teacher's Guide* on pages 7–9. Teachers should keep in mind, however, that evaluative activities can be overdone. Students who are often required to follow up their reading with exercises of one kind or another may dread finishing a book. Such exercises may seem like busywork to students—without relevance to them and their reading experiences.

Part 2: Vocabulary Building

Introduction

As most teachers are aware, reading improvement and vocabulary expansion are closely related, particularly at the lower levels. To promote vocabulary development, *Basic Reading Power 1* includes both direct instruction of useful vocabulary items and also instruction in vocabulary learning strategies. (An explanation of the rationale behind the approach to vocabulary in *Basic Reading Power 1* can be found on page 11 of the *Teacher's Guide*.)

The tests in this part reflect these two types of instruction. Some focus on specific words or phrases presented in these units. Many other tests, however, assess students' acquisition of the strategies they need to become independent vocabulary learners. This is a key aspect of the approach to vocabulary in *Basic Reading Power 1*. In particular, for students to expand their vocabularies in a serious way, they must make a habit of selecting and learning vocabulary on their own.

Notes:

- **Unit 2: Learning New Words from Your Reading**

  Tests 1 and 2: These do not test students in the usual way and cannot be graded like most tests since there are no right or wrong answers. These "tests" provide teachers with more exercises like those in the student book. Teachers can use them either for further practice or to evaluate how well students are able to follow the procedure for selecting and learning new words.

  Test 3: This serves as a model for teachers to use for testing students on the words they have chosen to learn. It is important for teachers to test students on these words so that students take the procedure seriously. Test 3 can be photocopied or copied by students onto a piece of paper. The format can be used repeatedly throughout the course to assess students' independent learning. Teachers should test students this way at the end of every unit of the student book. They can also ask students to select words or phrases from other readings (though not their extensive reading), and test them on those as well.

- **Unit 3: The 100 Words**

  The list of words has not been included with the tests. It can be useful for teachers to test students when students don't have the list in front of them so teachers can get a sense of how well students can produce the words on their own.

- **Unit 6: How Words Are Used Together**

  Tests 1–3: Teachers who feel that these tests are not challenging enough or who feel that they do not give an accurate assessment of students' abilities to produce targeted phrases, can block out the box of phrases when copying the tests. If they wish to give some help, but not to the extent of providing the phrases, teachers can block out the box and write part of the phrase in the blank. For the phrasal verbs, for instance, teachers can write just the preposition and ask for the verb. For the adverbial and prepositional phrases, they can write the first two letters of the phrase.

  Tests 7 and 8: These tests focus on relative pronouns and help students understand the meaning of a relative pronoun in a sentence. The tests (like the exercises) do not test students' abilities to produce original sentences with relative pronouns because this might not be appropriate for students at this level.

Part 2

List of Tests

	Type of Test*	Corresponding Exercise in Student Book		Type of Test	Corresponding Exercise in Student Book
Unit 1			**Unit 5**		
Test 1	S	Exercise 5	Test 1	V	Exercise 1
Test 2	S	Exercise 7	Test 2	V	Exercise 2
Test 3	S	Exercise 8	Test 3	V	Exercise 6
Test 4	S	Exercise 8	Test 4	V	Exercise 6
Unit 2			**Unit 6**		
Test 1	S	Exercise 3	Test 1	V	Exercise 2
Test 2	S	Exercise 3	Test 2	V	Exercise 3
Test 3	V	Exercise 3	Test 3	V	Exercise 4
Unit 3			Test 4	S	Exercise 6
Test 1	S	Exercise 5	Test 5	S	Exercise 6
Test 2	S	Exercise 6	Test 6	S	Exercise 8
Test 3	S	Exercise 7	Test 7	S	Exercise 9
Unit 4			Test 8	S	Exercise 10
Test 1	S	Exercise 5			
Test 2	S	Exercise 5			
Test 3	S	Exercise 8			
Test 4	S	Exercise 8			

*S = Skill or Strategy   V = Vocabulary

UNIT 1
Guidelines for Learning Vocabulary

Test 1

Find these words on the dictionary page. Write the parts of speech.

1. completely _____
2. complex _____
3. completeness _____
4. complexity _____
5. complaint _____
6. competitor _____
7. complete _____
8. complain _____

com·pet·i·tor /kəmˈpetətər/ *noun*
a person, team, company, etc., that is competing with another one: *Their main competitor is a large company that sells cheaper computers.*

com·plain /kəmˈpleɪn/ *verb*
to say that you are annoyed, not satisfied, or not happy about something or someone: *She decided to complain about the food to the manager because it was cold and tasted bad.*

com·plaint /kəmˈpleɪnt/ *noun*
a statement in which someone complains about something: *There have been a lot of complaints about the noise.*

com·plete¹ /kəmˈplit/ *adjective*
1 including everything or everyone: *This is a complete list of all the people in the class.* ANTONYM **incomplete**
2 in every way: *That class was a complete waste of time. I already knew about all that.*
3 finished: *Our research is almost complete. We will be finished this week.*
—**completeness** *noun*
➔ See Thesaurus box at **done²**

complete² *verb*
to finish doing or making something: *The book took five years to complete.*

com·plete·ly /kəmˈplitli/ *adverb*
in every way: *It's a completely new idea. Nobody's ever done this before.*

com·plex¹ /kəmˈpleks/ Ac *adjective*
something that is complex has a lot of different parts and is difficult to understand or deal with: *The human brain is very complex. Scientists don't fully understand it yet.* SYNONYM **complicated**
—**complexity** /kəmˈpleksəti/ *noun* the quality of being complex

com·plex² /ˈkɑmpleks/ Ac *noun*
a group of buildings or one large building used for a particular purpose: *My grandmother lives in an apartment complex for older people.*

UNIT 1
Guidelines for Learning Vocabulary

Test 2

Find each underlined word on the dictionary page. Write the part of speech and the meaning of the word in the sentence.

1. She <u>admitted</u> that she was wrong. But she didn't say she was sorry.

   Part of speech: _____

   Meaning: _____

   _____

2. The university <u>adopted</u> a new policy for foreign students.

   Part of speech: _____

   Meaning: _____

   _____

3. Only the best students are <u>admitted</u> to the college.

   Part of speech: _____

   Meaning: _____

   _____

4. My cousin <u>adopted</u> a sweet little girl from Texas.

   Part of speech: _____

   Meaning: _____

   _____

5. At some museums, <u>admission</u> is free on Sunday mornings.

   Part of speech: _____

   Meaning: _____

   _____

6. No one under 18 is <u>admitted</u> to the show.

   Part of speech: _____

   Meaning: _____

   _____

---

ad·mis·sion /əd'mɪʃən/ *noun*
1 the price you pay to go to a movie, museum, sports event, etc.: *Admission to the museum is $8.* | *an admission fee*
2 the right to become a student at a college or school: *Tom has applied for admission to City College.*
3 *formal* a statement or action that shows that something bad about yourself is true: *If he runs away from the police, people will consider it an admission of guilt.*

ad·mit /əd'mɪt/ *verb* **admitted, admitting**
1 to say that something is true, although you would prefer not to say it: *Okay, I admit (that) I was wrong — I shouldn't have lied.*
2 to allow someone to enter a place: *No one will be admitted to the game without a ticket.*

ad·o·les·cent /ˌædl'esənt/ *noun*
a young person between 12 and 17 years old who is becoming an adult: *At 15, Bill was a shy adolescent.*
—**adolescence** *noun* the time of your life when you are an adolescent: *Adolescence can be a difficult time because your body is changing and so are your responsibilities.*
→ See Thesaurus box at *child*

a·dopt /ə'dɑpt/ *verb*
1 to become the legal parents of a child that is not your own child: *The Bakers wanted to adopt a child because Christine could not become pregnant.*
2 *formal* to begin to use a new way of doing something: *The city has adopted a new method for reducing crime.*
—**adoption** /ə'dɑpʃən/ *noun* the act of adopting a child

UNIT 1
Guidelines for Learning Vocabulary

Test 3

Look at the dictionary page. Use the example sentences to help you find the information.

1. Write the verbs that are used with the noun *balance*.

   a) _____ her balance

   b) _____ off balance

   c) _____ a balance

2. Write the nouns or noun phrases that are used with the verb *balance*.

   a) balance _____

   b) balance _____

   c) balance _____

3. Write the prepositions that are used with the noun *balance*.

   a) _____ balance

   b) _____ balance

4. Write a noun that is used with the adjective *balanced*.

   balanced _____

5. Write a verb that is used with the adjective *bald*.

   _____ bald

---

balance /ˈbæləns/ *noun*
1 the ability to stand or walk steadily, without falling: *When the bus stopped suddenly, she almost lost her balance (=was unable to stay standing). | He hit me again when I was still off balance (=not standing steadily) and I fell down.*
2 a situation in which different things are in the right amounts or have the right amount of importance: *He was finding it difficult to strike a balance between family and work (=make sure that they had equal importance in his life).*
3 on balance = used when telling someone your opinion after considering all the facts: *On balance, I'd say it was a fair decision.*

balance *verb*
1 to put or have something in a steady position, or to be in a steady position: *She was balancing a plate of food on her knees and trying not to spill anything. | He turned slowly, trying to balance on one foot.*
2 to make sure that different things are in the right amounts or have the right amount of importance: *My mother was trying to balance her children's needs with the needs of her parents.*

bal·anced /ˈbæ|ənst/ *adjective*
including different things in the right amounts: *You should eat a healthy balanced diet with plenty of protein, fruits, and vegetables.*

bal·co·ny /ˈbælkəni/ *noun* plural **balconies**
1 a structure on the outside of a building, above ground level, where people can stand or sit: *She stood on the balcony looking up at the mountains.*
2 the seats upstairs in a theater

bald /bɔld/ *adjective*
if you are bald, you have little or no hair on your head: *He was going bald (=becoming bald) and decided to shave off all of his hair.*

UNIT 1
Guidelines for Learning Vocabulary

Test 4

Look at the dictionary page. Use the example sentences to help you find the information. (Include articles, pronouns, or other words if necessary.)

1. Write the nouns or noun phrases that are used with the adjective *even*.

   a) even _____

   b) even _____

   c) even _____

   d) even _____

   e) even _____

2. Write the nouns or pronouns that are used with the adjective *even* and the verb *be*.

   a) _____ 'll be even.

   b) _____ was very even.

3. Write a verb that is used with the adverb *evenly*.

   _____ evenly

4. Write prepositions that are used with the verb *even*.

   a. even _____

   b. even _____

5. Now write the nouns that are used after the verbs and prepositions.

   a. even _____

   _____

   b. even _____

   _____

e·ven /ˈivən/ *adverb*
1 used when adding something surprising: *He keeps everything, even old bus tickets.* | *The mountains always have snow on them, even in summer.*
2 used when making a comparison stronger: *Then he bought an even bigger car.*
3 even if = used when emphasizing that something will still be true if another thing happens: *I'll finish the job even if I have to work all night.*

even² *adjective*
1 flat, level, or smooth: *You need a large even surface to work on.*
2 an even rate, temperature, etc. does not change much: *Store the chemicals at an even temperature.*
3 divided equally, so that there is the same amount of something in each place, for each person, etc.: *Divide the dough into three even amounts.* SYNONYM **equal**
4 an even number can be divided exactly by two: *2, 4, 6, and 8 are even numbers.* ANTONYM **odd**
5 be even *informal* = to no longer owe someone something, especially money: *I paid five dollars more, so if you give me five dollars, we'll be even.*
6 a game or competition that is even is one where the teams are equal and as good as each other: *The first half of the game was very even — neither team scored.*
—**evenness** *noun*
—**evenly** *adverb* divided or spread equally: *Spread the frosting evenly over the cake.*
→ See Thesaurus box at **flat¹**

even³ *verb*
PHRASAL VERBS
even (something) out
if things even out, the differences between them become smaller: *The company is trying to even out the difference between the numbers of men and women (=make the numbers of men and women almost the same).*
even something up
to make something become equal or the same: *O'Malley hit a home run to even up the score.*

UNIT 2
Learning New Words from Your Reading

Test 1

A. Read the passage to the end.

Kangaroos, Part 1

When Europeans first arrived in Australia, they were afraid of kangaroos. They thought some kangaroos had two heads. In fact, these were mother kangaroos with their babies. Female kangaroos have big pockets, or pouches, on their stomachs. When baby kangaroos are born, they are very small. They climb into the pouches and start drinking lots of milk. After several months, the baby puts its head out of the pouch. That's when the mother kangaroo looks two-headed.

Kangaroos were strange to Europeans in other ways, too. Kangaroos stood up like men; they had heads like deer; and they hopped like frogs. In fact, no other large animal moves like a kangaroo. They have four legs, but they don't walk or run. They hop or jump on their back legs. They have very strong legs, so they can jump for long distances. They normally travel at about 13 to 16 miles per hour (20 to 25 kph). But when they need to go fast, they can go up to 44 miles per hour (70 kph).

European travelers wrote about kangaroos in their letters home. For some years, people in Europe didn't believe the travelers. Then in 1770, John Gore stopped in Australia. He was traveling around the world with Captain Cook. He shot a kangaroo and sent the head and skin back to England. Lots of people went to see this unusual animal.

B. Read the passage again. Underline the new words. Write five of them on the next page.

C. Look up the words in the dictionary. For each word, write the part of speech and the sentence where you found it. Then write the meaning of the word in that sentence.

1. Word: _____ Part of speech: _____

   Sentence: _____

   Meaning: _____

2. Word: _____ Part of speech: _____

   Sentence: _____

   Meaning: _____

3. Word: _____ Part of speech: _____

   Sentence: _____

   Meaning: _____

4. Word: _____ Part of speech: _____

   Sentence: _____

   Meaning: _____

5. Word: _____ Part of speech: _____

   Sentence: _____

   Meaning: _____

Show your work to another student. Did you write the same words and meanings? Then check your work with your teacher.

D. In your vocabulary notebook, write the words and the information about them. Then check the pronunciation and say the words and meanings aloud.

UNIT 2
Learning New Words from Your Reading

Test 2

A. Read the passage to the end.

Kangaroos, Part 2

Before Captain Cook arrived, kangaroos were already important to the Australian Aborigines. These are the people who lived in Australia before the Europeans arrived. The Aborigines had many stories about kangaroos. They ate kangaroo meat and used kangaroo skins and bones in many ways.

The Europeans who settled in Australia also hunted and ate kangaroos—many more than the Aborigines. But at the same time, the Europeans also helped the kangaroos in some ways. They cut down forests to make farms for sheep and cows. This made more space for kangaroos. The Europeans put water out for their cows and sheep. In dry weather, the kangaroos could drink this water, too. Finally, European farmers hunted and killed many dingoes. The dingo is a wild dog. It kills young sheep and also young kangaroos.

In Australia today, there are about 15 to 20 million kangaroos. Farmers say that there are too many. They say that the kangaroos take grass away from their animals. Some scientists don't agree with the farmers. They believe that kangaroos eat much less than sheep. The scientists say that kangaroos have soft feet, so they don't destroy grass the way sheep do. They think that kangaroos are not a problem for farmers.

But kangaroos are a problem on the roads. Kangaroos often move around to look for food. When they travel across the countryside, they cross roads. Sometimes they hop out suddenly onto roads when cars are coming. This causes terrible accidents every year.

B. Read the passage again. Underline the new words. Write five of them on the next page.

C. Look up the words in the dictionary. For each word, write the part of speech and the sentence where you found it. Then write the meaning of the word in that sentence.

1. Word: _____ Part of speech: _____

   Sentence: _____

   Meaning: _____

2. Word: _____ Part of speech: _____

   Sentence: _____

   Meaning: _____

3. Word: _____ Part of speech: _____

   Sentence: _____

   Meaning: _____

4. Word: _____ Part of speech: _____

   Sentence: _____

   Meaning: _____

5. Word: _____ Part of speech: _____

   Sentence: _____

   Meaning: _____

Show your work to another student. Did you write the same words and meanings?
Then check your work with your teacher.

D. In your vocabulary notebook, write the words and the information about them. Then check the pronunciation and say the words and meanings aloud.

UNIT 2
Learning New Words from Your Reading

Test 3

Vocabulary Quiz

Write ten new words or phrases from your vocabulary notebook. Then close your notebook and write the meanings.

New word/phrase   Meaning(s)

1. _____   _____

2. _____   _____

3. _____   _____

4. _____   _____

5. _____   _____

6. _____   _____

7. _____   _____

8. _____   _____

9. _____   _____

10. _____ _____

UNIT 3
The 100 Words

Test 1

A. Write in the missing letters for a word from the 100 Words list (or another word). Then write the word. There may be more than one correct answer.

1. s __ __ d   _____
2. wo __ __ d   _____
3. ot __ __ r   _____
4. d __ __ n   _____
5. th __ m   _____
6. t __ __ r e   _____
7. t __ __ s   _____
8. b __ __ n   _____
9. af __ __ r   _____
10. fi __ __ t   _____
11. i __ __ o   _____
12. p __ __ p l __   _____

13. kn __ __   _____
14. w __ y   _____
15. w __ __ k   _____
16. u __ e   _____
17. b __ c __ __ __ __ _____
18. m __ __ t   _____
19. t __ __ k   _____
20. tho __ g __ __   _____
21. wh __ __ h   _____
22. th __ __ k   _____
23. on __ __   _____
24. c __ __ ld   _____

B. Some of the words are missing from the conversation below. There is only the first letter. Write the other letters. (Use a word from the 100 Words list or another word)

Peter: W_____ are you doing h_____ in Chicago?
               1.   2.

Sasha: I'm studying a_____ the Music School.
                       3.

Peter: You a_____! I'll be th_____, too. I'm starting
              4.   5.

       i_____ September.
           6.

Sasha: Oh, really? I play clarinet. What a_____ you?
                                  7.

Peter: I play guitar. Jazz mostly, but I also l_____ blues. And
                                     8.

       y_____?
         9.

Sasha: Jazz and blues f_____ me, too. Hey, I play
                     10.

       w_____ a group o_____ friends
           11.   12.

       sometimes. We're meeting t_____ Saturday. You could
                            13.

       c_____ and bring y_____ guitar.
         14.   15.

Peter: Great! What t_____ and where?
                    16.

UNIT 3
The 100 Words

Test 2

Find 20 words from the 100 Words list (or other words) and circle them. (You can read across or down.) Then write the words below.

M	U	C	H	L	S	W	H	O	O
O	T	H	E	R	O	I	A	N	D
R	H	A	V	E	N	T	D	E	I
E	I	S	E	M	E	H	A	S	D
A	S	I	N	O	W	E	L	W	E
M	A	N	Y	R	O	T	H	E	R
A	Y	T	E	E	U	H	O	N	E
D	O	O	S	A	L	E	I	T	S
E	C	O	U	L	D	N	E	W	I

_____   _____   _____   _____

_____   _____   _____   _____

_____   _____   _____   _____

_____   _____   _____   _____

_____   _____   _____   _____

UNIT 3
The 100 Words

Test 3

A. Complete the fable "The Wolf and the Dog" with words from the 100 Words list (or other words). The first letter of each word is given. (You can also use words not on the list.)

One evening, a very hungry wolf came to a farm. He saw

s_____ chickens in the farm yard. He wanted to eat

1.

the chickens, but t_____ was a dog in the yard, too.

2.

The dog w_____ big and strong. The wolf didn't

3.

want to h_____ a fight with the dog. So he waited

4.

j_____ outside the yard.

5.

A_____ a while, a man came out of the farmhouse.

6.

He put some food out f_____ the dog and then went

7.

b_____ into the house.

8.

"Good evening," the wolf called to the dog.

"Good evening," s_____ the dog with his mouth full.

9.

The wolf said, "Do you g_____ that much food every

10.

d_____?"

11.

"T_____ times a day," said the dog. "I get breakfast in the

12.

morning and dinner in the evening." He ate some m_____.

13.

Then he looked at the wolf, "A_____ you hungry?"

14.

"Very hungry," said the wolf.

"Why don't you come live h_____ with me?" said the dog.

15.

This is a g_____ life. I watch the chickens for the farmer and

16.

he g_____ me food."

17.

The wolf sat d_____ near the dog. He

th_____, "Why not? If I stay here, I don't

h_____ to go hunting every night. He's right. It's an easy life."

But then he l_____ at the dog.

"What's t_____ under your ears?" he asked.

"What?" said the dog.

"Look at y_____ neck! It's all red!" said the wolf.

"Oh, that's nothing," said the dog.

"But doesn't it hurt? What's it from?"

"It's just the chain," said the dog. "During the d_____, the

farmer puts a chain on m_____ neck."

"A chain!" said the wolf. "You have to wear a chain!"

"That's right," said the dog. "But I don't care. I sleep

a_____ day, and in the evening he t_____

it off."

"Then no thank y_____, my friend," said the wolf. "I don't

w_____ a chain around my neck. Not

e_____ for a minute! Goodbye!"

And the wolf ran away, still hungry.

B. Look at the passage again. Find 10 more words from the 100 Words list and circle them.

UNIT 4
Guessing Meaning from Context

Test 1

Read the passage to the end. Think of words to complete the passage and write one word in each blank. (There may be more than one possible word.)

Livia Mazza is 89 years old. She lives in Bazzano, a small town in Italy. She

lives in the same house with her daughter and her two _____.
1.

Livia's son and his wife _____ in the next town.
2.

Livia helps her daughter with the _____. She also takes
3.

care of the children, and she works in the garden. She has flowers and vegetables

almost all year round. _____ the morning she walks to the
4.

store. Her house is near the village, so the store isn't _____.
5.

She buys milk and bread and other things for her family. She talks with the

_____ in the store and on the street. Everyone in Bazzano
6.

knows Livia, and she knows everyone.

UNIT 4
Guessing Meaning from Context

Test 2

Read the passage to the end. Think of words to complete the passage and write them in the blanks. (There may be more than one possible word.)

Salim Al Wahaibi is 12 years old. He lives in Al Mintirib, Oman. Oman is

a small _____ on the Arabian Sea. Salim has a 9-year-old

1.

brother, Talib. Five days a week, Salim and Talib go to _____.

2.

On the weekend, their life changes. Every weekend, there are camel races

near Al Mintirib. Salim's father has two camels. Because Salim and Talib are

small and light, they _____ the camels. There are many other

3.

camels with young riders. The boys all ride their camels to the starting line.

Then the camels start running _____. Salim's father drives a

4.

_____ next to the camels. He shouts at the camels and at his

5.

boys. The other fathers shout at their camels and their boys.

Then the race _____. But the boys can't stop the camels!

6.

The fathers have to run and stop them.

UNIT 4
Guessing Meaning from Context

Test 3

Read the context around each underlined word or phrase. Then write the part of speech and the general meaning. Don't use a dictionary

1. Are you going to the supermarket? Can you buy some orange juice for me? Get the kind that says <u>pure</u> orange juice. I don't like the other kinds. They have sugar and other things in them.

   Part of speech: _____

   General meaning: _____

2. What was that sound? Did you hear it? It came from behind the trees. It was very loud and very near. It sounded like the <u>roar</u> of a lion. But there aren't any lions here—or are there?

   Part of speech: _____

   General meaning: _____

3. One Sunday afternoon, we went to the movies. The movie was good, but the <u>audience</u> was terrible. It was full of children. They made a lot of noise, and I couldn't hear the movie.

   Part of speech: _____

   General meaning: _____

4. Aisha is 11 years old, and she likes to cook. She can make a cake <u>by herself</u>. She doesn't have to ask her mother for help, and she doesn't use cake mixes. Her cakes are very good, too.

   Part of speech: _____

   General meaning: _____

5. The teacher asked Tara the name of the longest river in the world. Tara didn't know the answer. Her friend Maike <u>whispered</u> it to her. But the teacher heard and got angry with both girls.

   Part of speech: _____

   General meaning: _____

6. Some people think the new art library is <u>ugly</u>. I don't agree. I think it's quite beautiful. It doesn't look like the old library, but that's a good thing. The old library was not nice-looking at all.

   Part of speech: _____

   General meaning: _____

UNIT 4
Guessing Meaning from Context

Test 4

Read the context around each underlined word or phrase. Then write the part of speech and the general meaning. Don't use a dictionary

1. That's a very interesting picture on the wall. It looks like a picture I saw by a famous artist. Is this by a famous artist, too? Then it's very <u>valuable</u>! You could sell it and get a lot of money.

    Part of speech: _____

    General meaning: _____

2. Peter lost his <u>wallet</u>. He says there wasn't much money in it. But there were some bus tickets and his ID card. He thinks it fell out of his pocket. Maybe someone will find it and give it back to him.

    Part of speech: _____

    General meaning: _____

3. Robert <u>dropped out</u> of high school in his last year. His parents wanted him to stay in school and finish. But he wanted to get a job and make some money.

    Part of speech: _____

    General meaning: _____

4. The <u>label</u> on this shirt says it's a medium. Usually I wear a medium, but this doesn't fit me at all. I think it's really a small.

    Part of speech: _____

    General meaning: _____

5. When the new president came out of the building, people <u>cheered.</u> He tried to speak, but there was too much noise. People were laughing, shouting and even singing.

    Part of speech: _____

    General meaning: _____

6. Yesterday we flew back from Japan. It was a night flight. I can usually sleep on night flights, but there was a small baby in front of us. It cried <u>off and on</u> all night, so I didn't get much sleep.

    Part of speech: _____

    General meaning: _____

UNIT 5
Word Parts

Test 1

Write the root, the prefix, and the meaning of the prefix. Then write the meaning of the word.

1. **unafraid**   Root: _____
   Prefix: _____ Meaning of prefix: _____
   Meaning of word: _____

2. **nonviolent**   Root: _____
   Prefix: _____ Meaning of prefix: _____
   Meaning of word: _____

3. **prehistoric**   Root: _____
   Prefix: _____ Meaning of prefix: _____
   Meaning of word: _____

4. **discontinue**   Root: _____
   Prefix: _____ Meaning of prefix: _____
   Meaning of word: _____

5. **misuse**   Root: _____
   Prefix: _____ Meaning of prefix: _____
   Meaning of word: _____

6. **underground**   Root: _____
   Prefix: _____ Meaning of prefix: _____
   Meaning of word: _____

7. **nonsense**   Root: _____
   Prefix: _____ Meaning of prefix: _____
   Meaning of word: _____

8. **unhealthy**   Root: _____
   Prefix: _____ Meaning of prefix: _____
   Meaning of word: _____

UNIT 5
Word Parts

Test 2

Write the root, the suffix, the part of speech of the root, and the part of speech of the root + suffix. Then write the meaning of the word.

1. **dirtiest**   Root: _____ Part of speech of root: _____

   Suffix: _____ Part of speech of root + suffix: _____

   Meaning of word: _____

2. **darkness**   Root: _____ Part of speech of root: _____

   Suffix: _____ Part of speech of root + suffix: _____

   Meaning of word: _____

3. **driver**   Root: _____ Part of speech of root: _____

   Suffix: _____ Part of speech of root + suffix: _____

   Meaning of word: _____

4. **helpless**   Root: _____ Part of speech of root: _____

   Suffix: _____ Part of speech of root + suffix: _____

   Meaning of word: _____

5. **useful**   Root: _____ Part of speech of root: _____

   Suffix: _____ Part of speech of root + suffix: _____

   Meaning of word: _____

6. **warmer**   Root: _____ Part of speech of root: _____

   Suffix: _____ Part of speech of root + suffix: _____

   Meaning of word: _____

7. **closely**   Root: _____ Part of speech of root: _____

   Suffix: _____ Part of speech of root + suffix: _____

   Meaning of word: _____

8. **careless**   Root: _____ Part of speech of root: _____

   Suffix: _____ Part of speech of root + suffix: _____

   Meaning of word: _____

UNIT 5
Word Parts

Test 3

Write the other forms of each word.

	Noun	Verb	Adjective	Adverb
1.	stranger	X		
2.			sad	
3.	sleep			
4.		open		
5.			dark	
6.	help			

UNIT 5
Word Parts

Test 4

Write the other forms of each word.

	Noun	Verb	Adjective	Adverb
1.	_____	anger	_____	_____
2.	sweetness	_____	_____	_____
3.	_____	X	_____	loudly
4.	_____	realize	_____	_____
5.	_____	_____	direct	_____
6.	_____	_____	free	_____

UNIT 6
How Words Are Used Together

Test 1

Complete each sentence with a phrasal verb from the box. Use each one only once.
(You may change the form of the verb.)

fall down	get out	lie down	put on	turn off
get off	get up	look up	take off	wait for

1. Jorge got his keys. He _____ on his coat and hat. He was ready.

2. When Mimi _____ the bus, she looked around. It was dark, and there weren't many people on the streets.

3. Peter forgot to _____ the water in the bathroom. It filled up the bathtub and went all over the floor.

4. The children usually _____ of school at 3:00. Then they take the school bus, and they're home by 3:30.

5. Some of the boys rode their bikes fast. Soon they were far ahead. But they stopped after a while to _____ the others.

6. It's easy to _____ information on the Internet. But I still like to use a dictionary for words.

7. My little brother _____ the stairs last night. He cried a lot, but he wasn't hurt.

8. If you go to bed very late, it's hard to _____ early.

9. They helped the old man _____ his old clothes and put on the new suit.

10. The doctors told the boy to _____. Then they put him in a special machine to take pictures of his head.

UNIT 6
How Words Are Used Together

Test 2

Complete each sentence with an adverbial phrase from the box. Use each one only once. (You may change the form of the verb.)

after a while	all the time	at last	on time
all day long	at first	for now	right away

1. The two girls were quiet _____. Then they began to talk about music. Soon they were good friends.

2. They arrived early in the morning, and they started working _____. They worked all day without stopping. But they still didn't finish before dark.

3. The poor little girl was not feeling well. She cried _____, and she didn't eat anything.

4. Jane waited all day for news from her daughter. _____, Lisa's husband called. Lisa was fine and the baby was fine: It was a girl.

5. It snowed _____ on Friday. Many people left work early. By evening, the cars and buses were all stopped.

6. The buses in this city are never _____. Every day I have to wait for a long time. I'm often late for work.

7. When Mary first arrived in China, she was afraid to speak Chinese. _____, she began trying to speak with people, and they usually understood her.

8. In a few years, we want to buy a house. But _____ we're living in an apartment near the university.

UNIT 6
How Words Are Used Together

Test 3

Complete each sentence with a prepositional phrase from the box. Use each one only once.

in back of	in the middle of	on the right
in front of	next to	on top of

1. The boy jumped into the water and began to swim. He was

   _____ the river when the police saw him.

2. Do you see that tall building over there? It's a new "green" building. There's a roof

   garden _____ it, with trees and flowers and grass.

3. We had an accident last night. We stopped at the red light. But the car

   _____ us didn't stop and they hit us.

4. The house was _____ the children's school. In the morning,

   they could stay in bed until late and run to school at the last minute.

5. There was a police car _____ her house. She saw it out the

   window, so she went out the back door.

6. This picture is very interesting. It shows some tall buildings in New York.

   _____ you can just see the Brooklyn Bridge.

UNIT 6
How Words Are Used Together

Test 4

Underline the subject and verb in each sentence. Write *S* under the subject and *V* under the verb.

1. Ho Kwangliang lives in Taichung, Taiwan.

2. He is the president of Hung Ming Enterprises.

3. His company makes parts of shoes.

4. Many shoe companies buy from Ho's company.

5. He does business with famous companies in the United States and Europe.

6. Hung Ming Enterprises makes $25 million every year.

7. There are four buildings with lots of machines.

8. One hundred people work in them.

9. Ho plans to open a new company in Shanghai, China.

10. That company will make shoelaces.

11. At first, Ho will work in Shanghai.

12. Then his son will take his place.

UNIT 6
How Words Are Used Together

Test 5

Underline the subject and verb in each sentence. Write *S* under the subject and *V* under the verb.

1. Maya has a job at a clothing company in Ecuador.

2. The company sells clothes to stores in the United States.

3. Maya works on the company's website.

4. Many people in the company use the website.

5. People outside the company use the website, too.

6. They look at the website to see the clothes.

7. Maya's work is important to the company.

8. Sometimes there are problems with the website.

9. She works hard and fixes the problems quickly.

10. Sometimes she stays late.

11. Maya's job is not easy.

12. But it's important to her and to the company.

UNIT 6
How Words Are Used Together

Test 6

Complete the passage with personal pronouns or possessive adjectives from the box.

Subject pronouns:	I	you	he	she	it	we	they
Object pronouns:	me	you	him	her	it	us	them
Possessive adjectives:	my	your	his	her	its	our	their

Rudy was a large, brown dog. He lived with Heinrich, a truck driver. Most of the time, Rudy and Heinrich were on the road. _____ had beds
1.
on the truck. _____ stopped at restaurants for their meals. On
2.
long drives, Heinrich didn't want to fall asleep, so _____ talked
3.
to Rudy and Rudy listened.

_____ home was in Hamburg, Germany, with Heinrich's
4.
sister Elena. At home, _____ slept a lot. Sometimes
5.
_____ went out for long walks or to see Heinrich's friends—
6.
always together.

One evening, Rudy and Heinrich didn't come home. In the morning, Elena
called Heinrich's friends. _____ didn't know anything. Then
7.
there was a noise at the door. Elena opened _____, and there
8.
was Rudy, alone.

Elena called the police. _____ told
9.
_____ that Heinrich was in the hospital. Elena went
10.
to the hospital. The doctors said that Heinrich had had a heart attack but
_____ wasn't in danger anymore.
11.

At home, Rudy was waiting for Heinrich. _____ sat by the
12.
door and didn't eat. The days went by. Heinrich had to stay in the hospital. Rudy
got thinner and thinner. Elena went to talk to Heinrich's doctor. "No dogs in the

hospital," the doctor said. But there was a little room near the door. Rudy could meet Heinrich in that room.

Elena brought Rudy to the hospital. _____ 13. was very thin and walked very slowly. But when _____ 14. saw Heinrich, _____ 15. jumped up and barked. People in the hospital were surprised to hear a dog.

After that, Rudy and Heinrich met every day. People soon knew Rudy's story. _____ 16. were glad to see _____ 17. at the hospital. Rudy started eating again and Heinrich got stronger. Soon _____ 18. were together again at home.

UNIT 6
How Words Are Used Together

Test 7

Underline the relative pronoun (*who*, *which*, or *that*) in each sentence. Then write the two ideas as two sentences.

1. She bought the sofa from Sharon, who is moving to California.

   _____

2. We stayed at a hotel that my brother stays at often.

   _____

3. Marie got an A on the chemistry exam, which was the most difficult one.

   _____

4. Today I finally got the letter that I was waiting for.

   _____

5. Maurice only likes bananas that are still green.

   _____

6. Zita opened the new computer that she bought in New York.

   _____

7. The night was very cold, which was not good for the plants.

   _____

8. Brian started talking to an old man who was sitting next to him.

   _____

UNIT 6
How Words Are Used Together

Test 8

Write the two sentences as one sentence. Use the relative pronoun.

1. Lang is going to the show. It starts at 10:00. (that)

   _____

2. He went to talk to the professor. She's teaching the course. (who)

   _____

3. Lisa lives in a nice part of Paris. It's full of good shops and restaurants. (that)

   _____

4. My friend and I visited Bulgaria. It's a very beautiful country. (which)

   _____

5. We often listen to that singer. She died last year. (who)

   _____

6. We didn't enjoy the weather. It was very hot. (which)

   _____

7. Walter buys meat. It comes from farms near here. (that)

   _____

8. Today we finally met the young people. They live next door. (who)

   _____

Part 3: Comprehension Skills

Introduction

In *Basic Reading Power 1*, reading comprehension is viewed as a complex process that involves a variety of skills. These include "bottom up" decoding skills, such as recognizing letters and words, matching letters/words with sounds, and following syntax, as well as "top-down" thinking skills, such as identifying topics and main ideas, making inferences, following the development of ideas, and applying logic. (This approach is explained more fully in the *Teacher's Guide*.)

In grading students' answers to these tests, teachers should keep in mind that the skills and strategies are part of a thinking process. Teachers should not simply look for "correct" answers. They should look for proof that students have understood and mastered the skill or strategy and should **accept answers that are different from those given in the Answer Key if students can justify them.**

Some of the units in this part include exercises that require students to write phrases or sentences for the answers. Evaluating these will require more time and effort on the part of the teacher than with multiple choice questions, but these open-ended answers will also allow teachers to get a better sense of students' thinking processes.

For each of the units in this part of the book, there are also two tests of the vocabulary that is presented in the Focus on Vocabulary sections in the student book. Rather than give students these tests immediately after they complete a given Focus on Vocabulary section, teachers are advised to wait a few days or a week to give the first one, and another week to give the second one. In this way, the tests will also serve as further rehearsal of the vocabulary items and reinforce students' learning of them.

Part 3

List of Tests

	Type of Test*	Corresponding Exercise in Student Book		Type of Test	Corresponding Exercise in Student Book
Unit 1			**Unit 4**		
Test 1	S	Exercise 2	Test 1	S	Exercise 4
Test 2	S	Exercise 3	Test 2	S	Exercise 4
Test 3	S	Exercise 9	Test 3	S	Exercise 5
Test 4	S	Exercise 10	Test 4	S	Exercise 6
Test 5	S	Exercise 11	FOV Test 5	V	Exercise 12
Test 6	S	Exercise 12	FOV Test 6	V	Exercise 12
FOV Test 7	V	Exercise 17	**Unit 5**		
FOV Test 8	V	Exercise 17	Test 1	S	Exercise 2
Unit 2			Test 2	S	Exercise 4
Test 1	S	Exercise 2	Test 3	S	Exercise 7
Test 2	S	Exercise 3	Test 4	S	Exercise 7
Test 3	S	Exercise 5	Test 5	S	Exercise 8
FOV Test 4	V	Exercise 10	Test 6	S	Exercise 9
FOV Test 5	V	Exercise 10	Test 7	S	Exercise 10
Unit 3			FOV Test 8	V	Exercise 16
Test 1	S	Exercise 4	FOV Test 9	V	Exercise 16
Test 2	S	Exercise 4			
Test 3	S	Exercise 8			
Test 4	S	Exercise 8			
Test 5	S	Exercise 12			
Test 6	S	Exercise 12			
FOV Test 7	V	Exercise 17			
FOV Test 8	V	Exercise 17			

*S = Skill or Strategy   V = Vocabulary

UNIT 1
Recognizing Letters, Words, and Phrases

Test 1

Look for words that <u>begin</u> with the key letters and circle them. Work as quickly as you can.

Key Letters

1. **so**	soon	slow	sorry	spot	soap
2. **sp**	spoon	slow	sport	speak	stop
3. **we**	where	went	wet	women	well
4. **br**	born	brown	bring	bird	burn
5. **ch**	child	cold	church	cheap	clean
6. **da**	dead	date	dirt	dark	drink
7. **dr**	dark	dirt	drive	dress	dear
8. **gr**	grow	ground	good	grass	girl
9. **th**	time	thing	thank	talk	touch
10. **to**	two	town	told	throw	touch
11. **pa**	past	play	pants	plant	part
12. **ma**	mean	many	make	meat	meal
13. **sh**	store	shoe	shot	sheep	sleep
14. **co**	cold	clock	color	cloud	could

UNIT 1
Recognizing Letters, Words, and Phrases

Test 2

Look for words that <u>end</u> with the key letters and circle them. Work as quickly as you can.

Key Letters

1. **ed**	bed	walked	farmer	read	closed
2. **sh**	much	wash	Spanish	cash	match
3. **ness**	darkness	careless	emptiness	sleepiness	helpless
4. **ly**	early	really	dirty	easy	loudly
5. **ks**	makes	parks	marks	markers	lakes
6. **ght**	fight	forget	white	light	night
7. **th**	watch	wash	math	south	that
8. **ld**	hold	good	gold	Ford	sold
9. **ing**	sang	eating	ring	winning	green
10. **est**	east	cleanest	best	desk	fast
11. **er**	worker	liked	doctor	baker	farmer
12. **ive**	wife	live	have	expensive	knife
13. **rn**	born	seen	learn	storm	modern
14. **ad**	sand	glad	bad	band	mad

UNIT 1
Recognizing Letters, Words, and Phrases

Test 3
Look for the word that does NOT rhyme with the key word and circle it.

Key Words

1. **look**	book	woke	took	cook	hook
2. **let**	eat	set	wet	pet	net
3. **star**	far	war	are	car	bar
4. **cat**	bat	sat	late	fat	rat
5. **son**	fun	sun	won	soon	gun
6. **red**	said	bed	dead	head	paid
7. **steak**	take	make	break	bake	speak
8. **free**	tree	she	lie	sea	we
9. **that**	bat	what	hat	cat	chat
10. **store**	hour	more	for	war	door
11. **green**	queen	been	seen	mean	teen
12. **hear**	beer	near	cheer	wear	fear
13. **seat**	feet	eat	date	sweet	sheet
14. **go**	do	know	no	slow	so
15. **hill**	fill	will	still	bill	mile
16. **die**	cry	buy	eye	lie	say
17. **then**	ten	seen	when	pen	men
18. **try**	lie	why	eye	say	buy

UNIT 1
Recognizing Letters, Words, and Phrases

Test 4

Look for the key word and circle it every time you see it. Work as quickly as you can.

Key Words

1. **said**	said	sad	sail	said	say
2. **time**	tame	time	tire	lime	time
3. **start**	star	smart	start	start	stare
4. **it**	if	in	it	is	it
5. **also**	also	also	alto	alas	alter
6. **our**	out	own	oar	our	our
7. **world**	word	world	would	world	wood
8. **through**	through	though	tough	trouble	through
9. **same**	some	same	sale	shame	same
10. **much**	mush	must	much	much	match
11. **way**	way	way	why	away	was
12. **than**	then	thaw	than	thin	than
13. **other**	often	otter	outer	other	other
14. **small**	small	smell	small	shall	smart

UNIT 1
Recognizing Letters, Words, and Phrases

Test 5
Look for the key phrase and circle it every time you see it. Work as quickly as you can.

Key Phrases

| 1. **get off** | get on | got off | get in | get off |
| | get off | go on | get off | get over |

| 2. **look up** | look up | look at | lock out | lock up |
| | luck out | look up | look up | look into |

| 3. **put on** | put on | put in | put on | put out |
| | put off | put on | part of | punt out |

| 4. **take off** | take in | take out | talk to | take off |
| | talk over | take off | take up | take off |

| 5. **find out** | found out | fend off | find out | find out |
| | friend of | find out | fine art | find it |

| 6. **get out** | get out | got us | get off | get out |
| | got out | get over | get our | got up |

| 7. **give up** | gave up | give out | give us | give in |
| | give up | give you | gave off | give up |

| 8. **go away** | go around | go away | gone away | go away |
| | go under | go after | go ahead | go away |

UNIT 1
Recognizing Letters, Words, and Phrases

Test 6

Look for the key phrase and circle it every time you see it. Work as quickly as you can.

Key Phrases

1. **in back of**	on backwards	in back of	a backup	in back of
	in balance	in bare feet	in back of	in battle
2. **up and down**	up and down	up in town	up and down	up a pound
	up and down	up or down	upside down	upload now
3. **in the world**	in a word	in the wood	in the world	in the world
	in the world	in a while	on the whole	in the wild
4. **right away**	right away	run away	right away	right of way
	rise in pay	right way	night away	right away
5. **on foot**	in first	on foot	in front	out front
	on foot	in focus	on foot	in force
6. **next to**	next to	nest to	next four	near to
	news for	nest of	next to	new to
7. **out of**	out into	out of	out for	on four
	out of	out at	out of	onto it
8. **on the right**	in the night	on the ride	in the right	on the right
	on the right	into the night	on the rise	out of rice

UNIT 1
Recognizing Letters, Words, and Phrases

Test 7

Look for the key phrase and circle it every time you see it. Work as quickly as you can.

Key Phrases

| 1. **no way** | not why | no wax | not wait | no way |
| | no way | no wear | no way | now away |

| 2. **by himself** | by herself | buy a shelf | by his wife | by himself |
| | by myself | by himself | by himself | buy and sell |

| 3. **at once** | at once | at one | an open | at once |
| | a touch | as often | at once | at noon |

| 4. **last year** | last yard | last year | less yield | last year |
| | last pear | less fear | last year | best year |

| 5. **how much** | how much | how must | have much | how much |
| | hot mush | how most | how much | hot lunch |

| 6. **once again** | once upon | one and | once again | one against |
| | one act | once again | only a gun | once again |

| 7. **by now** | by now | by now | buy now | buy new |
| | by name | by word | by now | by none |

| 8. **far away** | for a while | far away | far and wide | far away |
| | far away | for a way | for the way | for any |

UNIT 1
Recognizing Letters, Words, and Phrases

Test 8 Focus on Vocabulary

Make a check (✓) before the best meaning of the word.

1. successful
   a. _____ when someone makes you feel very angry
   b. _____ when you have done what you wanted to do
   c. _____ when you are thinking about what you are doing

2. tax
   a. _____ a job or thing you that you have to do
   b. _____ the business of buying and selling things
   c. _____ money you have to pay to the government

3. interested (in)
   a. _____ when you like doing something or you want to do it
   b. _____ feeling angry because you cannot do something
   c. _____ unusual or difficult to understand

4. smart
   a. _____ taking only a short time
   b. _____ pleased about something good
   c. _____ able to learn and understand things quickly

5. (in) trouble
   a. _____ feeling unhappy because you didn't do something
   b. _____ having a problem because of something you did
   c. _____ not getting something that you want

6. violent
   a. _____ using actions or words that hurt someone
   b. _____ done, or seen on a computer and not in the real world
   c. _____ not intelligent or showing good sense

7. funny
   a. _____ someone who talks to people a lot
   b. _____ something that you like a lot
   c. _____ something that makes you laugh

8. popular
   a. _____ liked by a lot of people
   b. _____ having a lot of money
   c. _____ different from other people

9. earn
   a. _____ spend money on expensive things
   b. _____ get money for the work you do
   c. _____ ask for money from a bank

UNIT 1
Recognizing Letters, Words, and Phrases

Test 9 Focus on Vocabulary

Complete the sentences. The first letter is given for each missing word. You may use a word only once.

1. People usually laugh at his movies because they're very
   f_____ .

2. The new boy is a problem. Sometimes he becomes v_____ and
   hurts other children.

3. When I was young, I was often in t_____ with my parents.
   They got angry with me almost every day.

4. Next year the state t_____ on gasoline will go up.

5. She was beautiful and very p_____ with the boys, but she was
   not well liked by the girls.

6. George is a very s_____ boy. At school he gets top grades in all
   his classes.

7. Roger Federer is a very s_____ tennis player. He wins many
   matches every year, and now he's a millionaire.

8. When Sara has time, she's always out taking pictures. She's very
   i_____ in photography.

9. When Elly started working, she didn't e_____ enough to live
   by herself.

UNIT 2
Scanning

Test 1

Scan the table of contents on page 47 for the answers to the questions. Work as quickly as you can.

1. Who wrote a story about a hunter?

   _____

2. How many stories are there in Part 1?

   _____

3. Which author is from France?

   _____

4. Which story is by Carlos Fuentes?

   _____

5. How many authors are from Canada?

   _____

6. On what page does the story "Everything" begin?

   _____

7. What is Part 3 about?

   _____

8. Where is the author Luisa Valenzuela from?

   _____

Short Stories from around the World

CONTENTS

UNIT 2
Scanning

Test 2

Scan the list of courses on page 49 for the answers to the questions. Work as quickly as you can.

1. What kind of songs will you learn in the voice course?

   _____

2. What time are the hip-hop dance classes?

   _____

3. Who is the instructor of the Latin dance class?

   _____

4. On what days are the meetings of the saxophone class?

   _____

5. What do you need for the piano class?

   _____

6. What should you wear to the hip-hop dance class?

   _____

7. What is the level of the saxophone class?

   _____

8. Which class is for couples only?

   _____

Corey Hill Center for Adult Education

Spring Courses

Music

Voice
Instructor: Domingo
Meetings: Wednesdays, 7:00 P.M. until 8:30 P.M.
Level: Beginner

In this class, you will learn about your voice and about making music. We will work on proper breathing and body position. Students can choose the songs to learn—traditional jazz, Broadway, or pop songs. Enjoy yourself and find your voice at last!

Piano for People with No Free Time
Instructor: Rubenstein
Meetings: Thursdays, 6:00 P.M. until 8:00 P.M.
Level: Beginner

A new method for playing jazz or pop music on the piano. You'll amaze your friends and have a great time. You won't learn note by note. You'll learn groups of notes, or chords. That's how the professionals play. All students need access to a piano.

Saxophone
Instructor: Coltrane
Meetings: Tuesdays, 6:30 P.M. until 8:00 P.M.
Level: Beginner to Intermediate

The saxophone is an American instrument and part of the American musical tradition. It can produce all kinds of sounds—soft and romantic, or wild and modern. You can learn how to play—it's not hard. We'll start with simple scales, and soon you'll be playing in a group. Bring a saxophone.

Dance

Hip-Hop Dance
Instructor: Shiraz
Meetings: Tuesdays, 7:00 P.M. until 8:30 P.M.
Level: Beginner

Hip-hop comes from a mix of funk, rock, rhythm and blues, and jazz musical styles. It is constantly changing on the streets and in music videos. In this class, we'll start with exercises to relax and feel the music. Then we'll move on to some dance steps. Wear comfortable clothing and gym shoes.

Latin Dances: Salsa, Merengue, and Bachata
Instructor: Villas
Meetings: Fridays, 8:00 P.M. until 10:00 P.M.
Level: Beginner to Intermediate

Here's your chance to learn three Latin dances. You'll learn the basic steps if you're a beginner, or more if you already know the basics. In a few weeks, you'll be stepping out onto the dance floor, ready for a good time. This class is for couples only.

UNIT 2
Scanning

Test 3

Scan the article on page 51 for the answers to the questions. Work as quickly as you can.

1. When were the Bryan brothers born?

   _____

2. How much money have they earned?

   _____

3. Where did they go to college?

   _____

4. What did their parents do (what job)?

   _____

5. How long will the Bryans continue to play tennis?

   _____

6. When did they become professionals?

   _____

7. What important tournaments did they win?

   _____

8. When did they start taking tennis lessons?

   _____

The Bryan Brothers—a Perfect Team

Bob and Mike Bryan are twins. One was born just two minutes after the other. They look the same, and they often act and think the same. But they aren't the same in everything. Mike is right-handed and Bob is left-handed.

Bob and Mike are professional tennis players. They play together on a doubles team (two people together). With a right-hander and a left-hander together, they can win points more easily.

In fact, the Bryans win a lot of points. They are one of the most successful doubles tennis teams in history. They have won almost 60 matches. They have earned more than $6 million.

The Bryans are both excellent tennis players, of course. But it helps to be twins. They don't even need to talk during matches because they know each other very, very well.

They were born in Camarillo, California, in 1978. Both their mother and their father were professional tennis players. The boys spent a lot of time on tennis courts when they were little. They started tennis lessons when they were four. When they were six, they won their first match.

Soon they were winning a lot of matches. They went to school together and then to college together, to Stanford University, in California. They both became stars on the tennis team. Then in 1998, they decided to become professionals. Professional tennis players have to travel a lot. It can be a very difficult and lonely life. But the Bryans are never alone. They always have each other. They play tennis together; they live together; they own a house together; they even have a bank account together.

In 2001, they decided to play only doubles. They were better at doubles than at singles. They wanted to become one of the best doubles teams in the world. And they did.

They have won a lot of important tournaments: the Australian Open, the French Open, the U.S. Open, and Wimbledon. They helped the U.S. tennis team win for several years. They have been the number one doubles players many times.

How long will they continue to play? Until at least 2012. They want to play in the Olympics again. Then maybe they will be ready to stop—and to change their lives. They might want to get married. Can they still live together when they are married? This is a question they can't answer now. For now, they just want to keep playing tennis.

UNIT 2
Scanning

Test 4 Focus on Vocabulary

Make a check (✓) before the best meaning of the word.

1. prize
   a. _____ a feeling of happiness and respect for yourself
   b. _____ the amount of money you must pay to buy something
   c. _____ something that you win in a competition or race

2. naturally
   a. _____ in a way that is usual or normal
   b. _____ when something bad almost happens to you
   c. _____ not trying to hide anything

3. teenage
   a. _____ less than 13 years old
   b. _____ between 13 and 19 years old
   c. _____ not young and not old

4. careful
   a. _____ without any problems or worries
   b. _____ thinking about what you are doing
   c. _____ not talking too much about yourself

5. career
   a. _____ the job(s) you have in an area of work
   b. _____ a business that makes or sells thing
   c. _____ an activity that you enjoy doing

6. private
   a. _____ not for other people to know about
   b. _____ having more money or better jobs
   c. _____ for anyone to know or use

7. joke
   a. _____ a report about something that happened
   b. _____ something funny that makes people laugh
   c. _____ a feeling of great happiness and pleasure

8. relative
   a. _____ a member of your family
   b. _____ someone you don't know well
   c. _____ a person you enjoy spending time with

9. continue
   a. _____ go back to a place where you were before
   b. _____ make someone or something do what you want
   c. _____ something that is happening and does not stop

10. several
   a. _____ a large number of people or things
   b. _____ more than a few but not a lot
   c. _____ exactly two in number

UNIT 2
Scanning

Test 5 Focus on Vocabulary

Complete the sentences. The first letter is given for each missing word. You may use a word only once. Each word should be in the right form for the sentence.

1. Mark's business c_____ began when he was still in college. He bought an old van and started a moving company.

2. You have to be very c_____ when you drive in the mountains. The roads are sometimes dangerous.

3. Jonah won first p_____ for his science project. His project was all about the weather.

4. N_____, the children all started talking when the teacher left the room.

5. Most of the old players are staying. But there are s_____ new players on the team this year.

6. There was a terrible noise outside, but the orchestra c_____ to play.

7. Karen's parents moved to Africa when she was young. She doesn't know her r_____ in England, not even her grandparents.

8. Miles's father likes telling bad j_____. No one laughs, but he doesn't care.

9. A t_____ girl won many tennis matches against older women.

10. In his p_____ life, he is a very different person. He isn't always laughing like he is on TV.

UNIT 3
Making Inferences

Test 1

Read these riddles about things you wear. Make inferences to answer the questions.

1. In the past, many people wore it every day.

   Now some people wear it in sunny weather.

   Other people wear it in cold weather.

   Some people never wear it. It's usually round.

   What is it? _____

2. In some places people never wear it

   In other places people wear it often.

   Both men and women wear it.

   It helps you stay dry. It usually has pockets.

   What is it? _____

3. In the past, it was always long.

   Now it can be long or short.

   It's like a dress, but less than a dress.

   Women don't always wear it these days. Only a few men wear it.

   What is it? _____

4. It's one thing.

   But we don't use the pronoun "it."

   In the past, women never wore them.

   Now many women often wear them. They can be long or short.

   What are they? _____

5. In hot places, people sometimes don't wear them.

   In cold places, people have to wear them.

   They can be made of different things.

   They can be very expensive. There are always two of them.

   What are they? _____

UNIT 3
Making Inferences

Test 2

Read these riddles about things in a house. Make inferences to answer the questions.

1. Every room has them.

   They are part of the house.

   They are taller than most people.

   They can be white or different colors. They often have open places in them.

   What are they? _____

2. It's part of the house.

   It's in every room.

   It's under everything.

   Sometimes it's hard and sometimes it's soft. It gets dirty, and you have to clean it often.

   What is it? _____

3. In some parts of the world, people don't use it.

   In most houses, there are several.

   You can use it for different things.

   There is usually one in the kitchen. It can be round or square.

   What is it? _____

4. Some kinds go on the wall.

   Other kinds go on tables or desks.

   It can be large or small.

   It can be noisy or quiet. People look at it often during the day.

   What is it? _____

5. In the past it filled a whole room.

   Then it got smaller and smaller.

   Now it fits inside a telephone.

   You can bring it with you everywhere. You can work with it, talk with it, or play with it.

   What is it? _____

UNIT 3
Making Inferences

Test 3

Read the conversation. Make inferences to answer the questions.

A: It's almost ready.

B: What is it?

A: There's spaghetti and some meat sauce.

B: Is that all?

A: All? There's a lot of spaghetti here. I don't want much, so it's mostly for you.

B: Is this the sauce? It looks funny. What's that green stuff?

A: I put in some green peppers.

B: Green peppers!

A: What's the matter? Don't you like them?

B: Only the red ones.

A: Oh, come on! You never like anything I make! You can just leave the peppers on your plate.

Now sit down and eat.

1. Where are these people? _____

2. Who are they? _____

3. What are they talking about? _____

4. How does each person feel? _____

UNIT 3
Making Inferences

Test 4

Read the conversation. Make inferences to answer the questions.

A: So how did it go?

B: Terrible.

A: Why?

B: I gave such stupid answers!

A: What did they ask you?

B: It was a woman. She asked about summer jobs. I tried to make them interesting. But what

can you say about being a waiter?

A: Didn't she ask you anything else?

B: Sure, she asked about my interests.

A: And what did you tell her?

B: I told her I love photography, and I take pictures for the school paper.

A: I'm sure she thought you were great. Don't worry. They'll take you.

B: Well, I'll find out soon. Anything important happen in class today?

1. Where are these people? _____

2. Who are they? _____

3. What are they talking about? _____

4. How does each person feel? _____

UNIT 3
Making Inferences

Test 5

Read the passage from "The Ring," by Marjorie Pemberton. Make inferences to answer the questions.

Lila drove through the gates and up the front drive. She parked her car under the big tree. As she rang the doorbell, tears came to her eyes. Megan answered the door, dressed as usual in her black dress and white apron.

"Hello, Megan" said Lila. "May I come in?"

Megan looked surprised. "Of course, Miss Prentice. But Mr. Shattuck is not home. He's in New York all week."

"I know. I'd just like to leave something for him."

"Of course. Please come in, Miss Prentice. I'm glad to see you."

"Thanks, Megan," said Lila. She walked past Megan and into Robert's office down the hall.

The smell of Robert—his cigarettes, his aftershave—was still in the room. On his desk, she saw the picture of the two of them together in Rome. They were standing in front of the Coliseum, smiling.

"I could still change my mind," Lila thought. Then she remembered the telephone call. She took the envelope from her bag. Inside it, she could feel the ring. It made a little noise as she put the envelope on Robert's desk. He would find it when he returned that evening.

1. Where are these people? _____

2. Who are they? _____

3. Who are the people in the picture on the desk?_____

4. What does Lila leave and why? _____

UNIT 3
Making Inferences

Test 6

Read the passage from "The Last Chance," by Sandra Shaw. Make inferences to answer the questions.

Jack opened the door to Room 22. It was late afternoon and the room was almost dark. He looked around quickly and quietly walked up to the front desk. He took the paper out of his pocket.

"I caught you!" said a voice.

Jack jumped and looked around. He couldn't see anyone. "Who's there?" he asked.

"You know who it is," said the voice. "Why are *you* here? It's late."

"I, um, forgot something. I'm getting it from my desk," answered Jack.

"Don't lie," said the voice. "Your desk is in the back. You were going up to Mr. Hamill's desk. I saw you at lunchtime. You took something from his desk. I know what it was."

"Uh, I didn't … I mean, I'm just … " Jack didn't know how to explain. "I'm not doing anything wrong."

"I know what you did. You took the test and now you're returning it. Now that you've copied it, right? You thought Mr. Hamill would never know. But you can't put it back now."

"But I didn't take the test!"

"That's what you say. We'll see what Mr. Hamill says. Tomorrow morning he'll look for the test and he won't find it. You were the last one to leave today, and he knows that."

1. Where are these people? _____

2. Who are they? _____

3. Who is Mr. Hamill? _____

4. What does the other person say Jack took from the desk? _____

UNIT 3
Making Inferences

Test 7 Focus on Vocabulary

Make a check (✓) before the best meaning of the word.

1. compete
   a. _____ look at something and see how it changes or moves
   b. _____ get more points in a game or competition
   c. _____ take part in a race or competition

2. decide
   a. _____ feel that you will be happy if you do something
   b. _____ choose what you are going to do
   c. _____ say that someone should do something

3. distance
   a. _____ the amount of space between two places
   b. _____ the way that someone or something is moving
   c. _____ the number of years that you have lived

4. weak
   a. _____ not young enough
   b. _____ not strong in your body
   c. _____ not ready to do something

5. train
   a. _____ prepare for a sports competition
   b. _____ go quickly from one place to another
   c. _____ follow someone to another place

6. mistake
   a. _____ something that you don't enjoy doing
   b. _____ something that is difficult to do
   c. _____ something that is not the right thing to do

7. miss
   a. _____ not like something or someone
   b. _____ not do something or be late for something
   c. _____ move someone from one place to another

8. record
   a. _____ the best that anyone has done
   b. _____ an idea that you have about something
   c. _____ instructions that tell you how to make something

9. adult
   a. _____ a person who is married
   b. _____ a person who is very old
   c. _____ a person who is not a child

10. moment
    a. _____ a particular point in time
    b. _____ an important thing that happens
    c. _____ a small copy of something

UNIT 3
Making Inferences

Test 8 Focus on Vocabulary

Complete the sentences. The first letter is given for each missing word. You may use a word only once. Each word should be in the right form for the sentence.

1. The Jamaican runner broke the Olympic r_____ for 100 meters.

2. Judy m_____ several classes last week because she was sick.

3. It was late, so we d_____ not to walk. We took a taxi.

4. At that m_____, the door opened and Gerald came running in.

5. In most sports, men don't c_____ against women.

6. What is the d_____ between Boston and New York?

7. I didn't mean to hurt her. It was all a terrible m_____.

8. The dinner party is for a_____ only. They don't want children making noise.

9. I always have breakfast. If I don't, I feel quite w_____ by noon.

10. My brother wants to be in the bicycle race next month. He is t_____ for it every morning before work.

UNIT 4
Focusing on the Topic

Test 1

Read each list. Then write a topic.

1. Argentina   Brazil   Venezuela   Chile   Colombia
   Topic: _____

2. biology   chemistry   physics   astronomy   geology
   Topic: _____

3. television   computer   DVD player   MP3 player   radio
   Topic: _____

4. doors   roof   windows   walls   rooms
   Topic: _____

5. butter   milk   ice cream   cheese   yogurt
   Topic: _____

6. author   journalist   blogger   poet   reporter
   Topic: _____

7. me   you   them   us   him
   Topic: _____

8. Yumiko   Marisol   Moira   Catherine   Anne
   Topic: _____

9. Toyota   Mercedes   Ford   Fiat   Hyundai
   Topic: _____

10. toilet   shower   mirror   sink   bathtub
    Topic: _____

UNIT 4
Focusing on the Topic

Test 2

Read each list. Then write a topic.

1. Toronto   Montreal   Vancouver   Quebec   Ottowa

   Topic: _____

2. inch   gallon   pound   mile   foot

   Topic: _____

3. Rio Grande   Ganges   Yangtze   Amazon   Nile

   Topic: _____

4. hat   gloves   boots   scarf   coat

   Topic: _____

5. check-in   gate   security   baggage claim   customs

   Topic: _____

6. cleaning   washing   cooking   ironing   vacuuming

   Topic: _____

7. game shows   news   movies   sports   cartoons

   Topic: _____

8. Black   Caribbean   Baltic   Adriatic   Bering

   Topic: _____

9. front desk   lobby   elevators   meeting rooms   guest rooms

   Topic: _____

10. mountains   forests   hills   plains   desert

   Topic: _____

UNIT 4

UNIT 4
Focusing on the Topic

Test 3

Read each list and write a topic. Then add one more word to the list.

1. comma   colon   question mark   exclamation point   _____
   Topic: _____

2. tables   menu   plates   food   _____
   Topic: _____

3. mayor   king   governor   prime minister   _____
   Topic: _____

4. swimmers   boats   shells   sand   _____
   Topic: _____

5. eleven   forty-four   sixty-six   twenty-two   _____
   Topic: _____

6. library   classrooms   offices   dining hall   _____
   Topic: _____

7. actors   lights   director   photographer   _____
   Topic: _____

8. Clinton   Roosevelt   Bush   Obama   _____
   Topic: _____

9. goldfish   parrot   turtle   cat   _____
   Topic: _____

10. highway   lane   street   avenue   _____
    Topic: _____

UNIT 4
Focusing on the Topic

Test 4

One word in each list does not belong to the topic. Cross out the word that doesn't belong. Then write the topic.

1. Ireland   Japan   Madagascar   Morocco   Cuba

   Topic: _____

2. Earth   Venus   Mars   Saturn   Sun

   Topic: _____

3. wheels   doors   chain   seat   pedals

   Topic: _____

4. circle   square   rectangle   cube   triangle

   Topic: _____

5. window   drawing   photograph   painting   poster

   Topic: _____

6. microwave   fridge   coffeemaker   hair dryer   dishwasher

   Topic: _____

7. tail   nest   wings   windows   engines

   Topic: _____

8. players   baskets   fans   ball   table

   Topic: _____

9. surfing   snow skiing   swimming   sailing   diving

   Topic: _____

10. flour   fish   sugar   butter   milk

   Topic: _____

UNIT 4
Focusing on the Topic

Test 5 Focus on Vocabulary

Make a check (✓) before the best meaning of the word.

1. take care of
   a. _____ look at something to see if it is correct
   b. _____ do things for someone who is very young, old, or sick
   c. _____ take something in your hands

2. cousin
   a. _____ a person related to you, but not in your close family
   b. _____ a person who marries someone in your family
   c. _____ a person who knows you and your family well

3. rent
   a. _____ take something away from a place
   b. _____ get money for a job or service
   c. _____ pay money to live in a place

4. outside
   a. _____ not in a building, room, city, country, or group
   b. _____ parts of a city that are far from the center
   c. _____ without a home or place to live

5. notice
   a. _____ want or need someone or something
   b. _____ see, feel, or hear someone or something
   c. _____ seem to be something or have something

6. invite
   a. _____ ask someone to come for a party or visit
   b. _____ talk to someone about what they want to do
   c. _____ put people or things into an order

7. camp
   a. _____ a field for growing plants or animals
   b. _____ a small city or town near the sea
   c. _____ a place where people stay and do special activities

8. accident
   a. _____ the things that are happening in someone's life
   b. _____ something bad that happens, not wanted or planned
   c. _____ something that you do in a regular way

9. headache
   a. _____ when you can't see well
   b. _____ the top or front of something
   c. _____ when your head hurts

10. amount
   a. _____ how good something is
   b. _____ something that is very large
   c. _____ how much of something

UNIT 4
Focusing on the Topic

Test 6 Focus on Vocabulary

Complete the sentences. The first letter is given for each missing word or phrase. You may use a word or phrase only once. Each word or phrase should be in the right form for the sentence.

1. There was an a_____ at the airport yesterday, but no one was hurt.

2. You can't go in the store with an ice-cream cone. You have to wait o_____ until you finish it.

3. Who will t_____ your children while you are away?

4. Jordan didn't n_____ the sign. It was behind some trees.

5. On Thanksgiving Day, we always have dinner with my c_____.

6. When I get a bad h_____, I have to go lie down.

7. All the soldiers had to go a special c_____ for three months.

8. This summer, we are r_____ a little house in the mountains.

9. He asked for financial aid (money) from the college, but he got only a small a_____.

10. Only a few students were i_____ to meet the president.

UNIT 5
Understanding Paragraphs

Test 1

Read the passages. Are they paragraphs? Check (✓) your answer.

Interesting Houses

1   Greg Breeze's house looks like other houses in California. It's white, and it has a garage. In California, houses are often very expensive. Many famous actors live in California, too. In America, most houses are made of wood. Some houses are made of stone. There are many stone walls in some parts of the country. Many houses have big yards and lots of trees.

Paragraph _____   Not a paragraph _____

2   The Inuit people live in Northern Canada. It is very cold there. In winter, they sometimes build houses the old way. These houses are called igloos. They are made of snow. The Inuit use large pieces of hard snow to make a circle. Then they build walls and a roof, all of snow. The snow walls keep the cold wind out. Inside, the Inuit light a fire and soon the igloo is very warm.

Paragraph _____   Not a paragraph _____

3   Some of the people of Mongolia live in houses called yurts. They build their yurts with wood and animal skins. Yurts are light and easy to carry. These Mongolian families don't live in one place all the time. They travel with their animals. A family can take down their yurt and carry it with them. Then they put it up in a new place. This way they have a new home ready in a short time.

Paragraph _____   Not a paragraph _____

4   The Great Wall of China was built about 500 years ago. There are houses under the wall. People in different parts of China make different kinds of houses. Some parts of China are warm and some are very cold. India is also a very large country. There are many different kinds of houses in India. The Taj Mahal was built about 350 years ago. Many people go to India to see it.

Paragraph _____   Not a paragraph _____

UNIT 5
Understanding Paragraphs

Test 2
Read each paragraph and circle the best topic.

People's Names

1   In different countries there are different ideas about last names. In some countries—for example, the United States—a married woman usually takes her husband's last name. Their children use that name, too. In other countries, married women keep their own last name. This is true in Vietnam, Italy, Spain, and some South American countries. In these countries, the children usually take the father's last name. But sometimes they use two last names, one from the mother and one from the father.

   a. last names in the United States

   b. last names around the world

   c. the names of married women

2   In Calcutta, India, most people have two first names. One first name is put on the papers when a child is born. It's called the "good" name, and it's used mostly outside the home. This is the name that is used at school and at work. The people who use this name usually don't know the person well. The other name is called the "pet" name. It's used mostly at home by people in the family.

   a. first names in Calcutta

   b. the pet name at home

   c. names in India

3   Do you have a name you don't like? If you live in the United States, you can change it. There are some rules about changing your name. You can't change your name if you have problems with the police. You also can't change your name if you are less than 18 years old. But if you are 18 and you are not in trouble, you can go to a special government office. You have to fill out some papers and sign a form. After that, you have a new name. Then you have to tell everyone to use your new name.

   a. people and their names

   b. the office for changing your name

   c. changing your name in the United States

UNIT 5
Understanding Paragraphs

Test 3

Read each paragraph and write the topic.

Vacations

1   Not everyone wants to rest on their vacation. Some people like to do exciting things. These people sometimes go on adventure travel vacations. They bicycle from town to town in a foreign country. They go down rivers on boats. Or they walk for many days in the mountains. Some people even like their adventures to be a little dangerous. These people may try to climb a very high mountain. Or they may try to walk across a desert.

Topic: _____

2   A cooking vacation is for people who like to cook and to travel. There are many cooking schools around the world. You can go to a new city and take a class at one of these schools. For example, you can go to Venice and learn how to make Italian food. Or you can go to Hong Kong and learn how to make Chinese food. On cooking vacations, you eat a lot of good food. But these vacations are not only about the food. You will also meet new people and see new places.

Topic: _____

3   Another kind of vacation is all about animals and nature. The African safari is an example of this kind of vacation. On a safari, you may see lions, zebras, giraffes, and many other animals. Africa is not the only place to watch wild animals. In Costa Rica, you can climb into tall trees and watch birds, snakes, and monkeys. In Australia, you can see kangaroos, koalas, and wallabies. And finally, in many places, you can watch animals in the water. In the Caribbean, you can go look at beautifully colored fish. In the Atlantic or Pacific, you can watch dolphins and whales.

Topic: _____

UNIT 5
Understanding Paragraphs

Test 4

Read each paragraph and write the topic.

Furniture

1   Many people work for long hours at a table or desk. For them, a comfortable chair is very important. An uncomfortable chair can cause a lot of problems. The most common problem is a backache (your back hurts). Your legs or arms can also start hurting. What makes a chair comfortable? It should be high enough, but not too high. It should be soft, but not too soft. And it should help you sit correctly. Your back should be straight.

Topic: _____

2   In developed countries, people usually have a dining table in their homes. It may be in the kitchen or it may be in a different room—the dining room. It may be round or square. This is where the family eats meals most of the time. In Western countries, the dining table is usually quite high. It's just right for people sitting in chairs. In some Eastern countries, the dining table is much lower. That's because people don't usually sit in chairs when they eat. They sit on cushions on the floor.

Topic: _____

3   You can learn a lot from the furniture in a house or apartment. It's like clothes on a person. It tells you about the people who live there. If people have expensive furniture, they probably have a lot of money. If the furniture is beautiful, they have good taste, and they care about the things around them. If it's old, that may mean the people don't have much money. Or it could mean that they don't care about the things around them.

Topic: _____

UNIT 5
Understanding Paragraphs

Test 5

Complete each paragraph with a sentence from the box. Write the letter of the correct sentence on the line in the paragraph. Then write the topic.

---

a. Others used to be war dances
b. For hundreds of years they were alone on the islands
c. In fact, many famous movies have been made there

New Zealand

1   The first people in New Zealand were the Maori people. They came to the islands about 1,000 years ago. They lived by fishing and farming. _____. Then people from Europe came to New Zealand in the 19th century. Many Maori people got sick and died. Many others lost their land. Now only about 14 percent of the people in New Zealand are Maori. They are the poorest people in the country, and they have many problems. But they are an important part of the country's history and way of life.

Topic: _____

2   The Maori people have a dance called the *haka*. There are many kinds of *haka* dances. Some of them tell old Maori stories. _____. In the dances, people move their hands and eyes around, and they open their mouths wide. In New Zealand today, people still like to do *haka* dances. Some say it makes them feel strong, and others say it makes them feel happy. In fact, some New Zealand sports players do a *haka* dance before every game.

Topic: _____

3   These days millions of people see New Zealand, but they don't know it is New Zealand. That's because they see it in the movies. New Zealand is a very beautiful country. It has many different kinds of land, from high mountains to rocky seaside. It also doesn't have very many people, so there are lots of wild, open places. For these reasons, it's a good place to make movies. _____. For example, *The Lord of the Rings* movies were all made there.

Topic: _____

UNIT 5
Understanding Paragraphs

Test 6

A. The sentences below are from paragraphs about two topics. Write the letter of the topic after each sentence.

   a. **The job of a city bus driver**

   b. **The job of a city police officer**

   1. They try to help the traffic move through the city. _____

   2. They have to be ready to stop quickly. _____

   3. People on the buses get angry because they move slowly. _____

   4. They also try to stop bad people from hurting others. _____

   5. Bus drivers hate the traffic, too. _____

   6. Some of them are traffic police. _____

   7. They have to watch the road carefully all the time. _____

   8. They try to stop bad people from breaking into homes or stores. _____

   9. In the morning and the evening, the buses are often stopped in traffic. _____

   10. Other police officers work to stop crime. _____

B. **Now complete the paragraphs with sentences from part A. Put the sentences in logical order. (More than one order is possible.)**

   1. The job of a bus driver is not easy in the city.

   _____

   _____

   _____

   _____

   _____

   2. Police officers have many kinds of jobs in the city.

   _____

   _____

   _____

   _____

   _____

UNIT 5
Understanding Paragraphs

Test 7

In each paragraph there is one extra sentence. It is not about the topic. Find the sentence and cross it out. Then write the topic.

Pets

1   Some people say that cats are better pets than dogs. First, cats are cleaner. They don't get dirty, and they don't make the house dirty like dogs. Also, cats almost never hurt people, but dogs sometimes bite. Some dogs even kill people. Cats are quieter than dogs, too. The police never get phone calls about noisy cats! Some dogs have funny names. And finally, cats are easy to take care of. You have to take a dog out for a walk every day, but you don't have to take out a cat.

Topic: _____

2   What kind of pet is right for you? One thing to think about is where you live. If you live in a house with a large yard, you can get a large dog. A house with a large yard is expensive. But if you live in a small apartment, you should get a small pet. That could be a small dog or a cat. Another important question is about time. If you don't have much free time, you shouldn't get a dog. Cats take less time to care for. You also shouldn't get a dog if you travel a lot. You can leave a cat alone for two or three days, but you can't leave a dog alone for very long.

Topic: _____

3   Dogs are often called "man's best friend." In fact, they can be very good company. Most dogs like to be with people. They often want to play or get attention—just like children. For this reason, they can make life better for many people. This is especially true for older people who live alone. Dogs usually don't like cats. Dogs can also help take care of people. Special dogs help people who can't see. Other dogs help children with certain problems. These children are unhappy with other children or adults. But they feel happy with dogs.

Topic: _____

UNIT 5
Understanding Paragraphs

Test 8 Focus on Vocabulary

Make a check (✓) before the best meaning of the word.

1. peace
   a. _____ a situation that is quiet and calm
   b. _____ a part of something larger
   c. _____ a hole in the middle of something

2. director
   a. _____ a person who likes to tell other people what to do
   b. _____ someone who writes books or movies
   c. _____ the person who tells the actors what to do in a movie

3. grow up
   a. _____ start school
   b. _____ become an adult
   c. _____ have children

4. partner
   a. _____ a friend or classmate
   b. _____ the person you live with
   c. _____ a father or mother

5. actress
   a. _____ someone you have met before
   b. _____ something you want to do
   c. _____ a woman in a movie or on television

6. dream
   a. _____ something you hope will happen
   b. _____ exciting things that happen
   c. _____ a strong feeling about something

7. able to
   a. _____ like
   b. _____ should
   c. _____ can

8. really
   a. _____ only, just
   b. _____ truly, in fact
   c. _____ not long ago

9. energy
   a. _____ pleasure you get from doing something
   b. _____ someone who hates you and wants to harm you
   c. _____ physical and mental strength

10. recognize
    a. _____ know someone because you've seen them before
    b. _____ say that someone should do something
    c. _____ put a name or details on an official list

UNIT 5
Understanding Paragraphs

Test 9 Focus on Vocabulary

Complete the sentences. The first letter is given for each missing word. You may use a word only once. Each word should be in the right form for the sentence.

1. I saw that a_____ in another movie last year. She's very good.

2. He and his p_____ moved to Los Angeles last year. They plan to get married in the spring.

3. After lunch, I don't have much e_____, so I often lie down and rest.

4. She sat in the park and enjoyed the p_____ and quiet.

5. I r_____ don't understand what you are talking about.

6. There he was in the picture of all the students. I r_____ his red jacket.

7. His d_____ was to meet the president and shake his hand.

8. After she fell from her horse, Paula wasn't a_____ to walk well.

9. Her children g_____ up and left home. After that she lived alone with her cat.

10. The d_____ of that movie is American. She made several good movies about war.

Part 4: Thinking in English

Introduction

The exercises in Part 4 aim to give students practice in following the language and the logic that writers use to express their ideas in English. In order to complete the exercises correctly, students will need to make use of some of the skills and strategies they learned in Parts 2 and 3. (See the *Teacher's Guide* for a more complete explanation.)

The exercises are grouped into three Units within which the exercises become progressively more difficult. Students should be tested only after they have completed the corresponding exercises.

Note: Students should not use dictionaries while doing these tests.

List of Tests

	Type of Test*	**Corresponding Exercise in Student Book**
Unit 1		
Test 1	S	Exercise 8
Test 2	S	Exercise 8
Unit 2		
Test 1	S	Exercise 8
Test 2	S	Exercise 8
Unit 3		
Test 1	S	Exercise 8
Test 2	S	Exercise 8

*S = Skill or Strategy   V = Vocabulary

UNIT 1: LEVEL 1

Test 1

Circle the best answer.

1. Many students use the library in town. They go there because it's quiet. It's a good place to _____.

   a. talk   c. eat

   b. play   d. study

2. Our car is very small. We can't carry friends in it, and we can't put a bicycle in it. We need to get _____.

   a. a smaller car   c. a bigger car

   b. new friends   d. another bicycle

3. Fishing is not always very exciting. Some days when you go fishing nothing happens. You wait for a very long time, but you _____.

   a. get lots of fish   c. don't get any fish

   b. get some help   d. don't get hungry

4. Do you like to read mystery stories? Many people like Agatha Christie's mysteries. She knew how to _____.

   a. write a love story   c. read a good book

   b. tell a good story   d. talk about people

5. Most people don't want to live near an airport. They don't want to hear airplanes all day long. The big planes are _____.

   a. very loud   c. very fast

   b. too expensive   d. too far away

6. Some doctors say that green tea is good for you. It's a good idea to drink green tea every day. It's good for your teeth, and it helps you _____.

   a. get sick   c. stay home

   b. stay well   d. get ready

UNIT 1: LEVEL 1

Test 2

Circle the best answer.

1. Do you know where Martin lives now? I need his new address. Last week, I sent him a letter and it came back to me. The address I had for him was _____.

   a. right   c. new

   b. wrong   d. short

2. Many famous baseball players are from the Dominican Republic. Why is this? Because everyone loves baseball there, and the boys play it _____.

   a. all the time   c. on Tuesdays

   b. sometimes   d. a few times

3. Szilvia is from Hungary. Last year, she went to London to learn English. This year, she's going to Paris to learn French. Szilvia likes _____.

   a. living in London   c. working in Paris

   b. staying in Hungary   d. learning languages

4. These days, you can do lots of things on a cell phone. You can take pictures and send email or text messages. You can even watch a movie _____.

   a. at the cinema   c. on a cell phone

   b. on a DVD player   d. at home

5. In World War I, guns were not the biggest killers. The biggest killer was disease. Many people got sick and died. In those days, doctors _____.

   a. couldn't save them   c. had good medicines

   b. didn't get sick   d. were also soldiers

6. When you take medicine, you should be careful. On the box, you can find out about the medicine. You want to be sure the medicine is right for _____.

   a. you   c. your doctor

   b. women   d. a day

UNIT 2: LEVEL 2

Test 1

Circle the best answer.

1. Karsten lives in Amsterdam. He travels around the city a lot for work. He always rides his bicycle or takes the bus. He never drives because he doesn't _____.
   a. have a bicycle
   b. like the city
   c. have a car
   d. work at home

2. In London there are many video cameras. They take videos of people on the streets. If something happens, the police look at the videos. They can sometimes see _____.
   a. what happened
   b. who was talking
   c. lots of cars
   d. famous people

3. In a bad storm, there is sometimes a lot of wind, rain, snow, or ice. The roads can be dangerous. It's a good idea to _____.
   a. take a walk
   b. drive your car
   c. open the window
   d. stay home

4. Last year, Rex and Lynette had a small house with trees around it. Then a terrible storm came—a tornado. Now there's no house and no trees. There's just _____.
   a. a big hole
   b. another storm
   c. a small town
   d. their house

5. Cell phones are helping lots of small businesses in Africa. Farmers, fishermen, and shop owners all use them. With cell phones, they can learn about prices, and they can _____.
   a. catch fish
   b. talk with friends
   c. grow food
   d. talk to buyers

6. When people get older, their eyes change. They may still see things far away. But they can't see things that are very near. They often have trouble _____.
   a. speaking
   b. reading
   c. sleeping
   d. eating

UNIT 2: LEVEL 2

Test 2

Circle the best answer.

1. Police dogs are very good at finding people. They can find people who are hiding from the police. They can also find people _____.
   - a. who are lost
   - b. with cats
   - b. with no home
   - c. at work

2. In some countries people can't get clean water at home. For good drinking water, they have to walk a long way. Or they have to pay for _____.
   - a. Coca-Cola
   - c. good food
   - b. dirty water
   - d. bottled water

3. It's not always easy to shop in a very big supermarket. There are so many things in the store. Sometimes it's hard to find what you want. And sometimes it's _____.
   - a. fun to shop
   - c. hard to choose
   - b. easy to pay
   - d. not expensive

4. Penguins are birds that can't fly. They also can't run very fast because they have short legs. They spend a lot of time in the water, so they are very good at _____.
   - a. flying
   - c. walking
   - b. swimming
   - d. singing

5. In the past, Manhattan (New York) had lots of hills. The Lenape Indians lived on the hills. Then the English and Dutch arrived. They took off the tops of the hills and filled up the low places. Now there are _____.
   - a. even taller hills
   - c. lots of hills
   - b. no more people
   - d. no more hills

6. In Mara's family, everyone eats breakfast at a different time. They are usually out at lunch. But they are all home at dinnertime. They usually cook dinner and eat it _____.
   - a. alone
   - c. together
   - b. at a restaurant
   - d. in the morning

UNIT 3: LEVEL 3

Test 1

Circle the best answer.

1. In the past, only boys played sports at school, and only men played sports for money. Now things are very different. Many young girls play sports at school, and many women _____.
   a. play music for money
   b. pay money for sports
   c. watch men play sports
   d. play sports for money

2. Last winter, Nina visited Fargo, North Dakota. She wanted to take pictures of the city, but it was too cold. Her camera didn't work outside. She could only take pictures _____.
   a. inside
   b. of friends
   c. outside
   d. of houses

3. Yellowstone Park in Wyoming is very big and beautiful. It's also full of wild animals. You can watch the animals, but you shouldn't go near them. Some of them can be _____.
   a. far away
   b. dangerous
   c. friendly
   d. hungry

4. Antarctica is the coldest place in the world. It's too cold for most plants. But there is one kind of plant that can live there. Scientists are interested in this plant. They want to know _____.
   a. why it is so cold
   b. who lives there
   c. how it lives there
   d. where it grows

5. In the high mountains, cooking is different. Everything takes more time. For example, when you cook rice, it usually takes 15 minutes. In the mountains, it takes _____.
   a. 8 minutes
   b. 20 minutes
   c. a bigger pot
   d. much less time

6. Cary Grant was a famous movie star from the 1930s to the 1950s. In some of his movies, he was very funny. He had a serious face, but he could _____.
   a. make people laugh
   b. look very sad
   c. make people cry
   d. speak very fast

UNIT 3: LEVEL 3

Test 2

Circle the best answer.

1. Amsterdam and Venice have one thing in common. They both have lots of canals (human-made rivers). People have to get across the canals, so Amsterdam and Venice also have a lot of _____.
   - a. roads
   - b. bridges
   - c. tourists
   - d. water

2. Desert plants are very special. They only have flowers when it rains. But in the desert, it doesn't rain very often. It may not rain for years. Then, after it finally rains, the desert is full of _____.
   - a. sand
   - b. rocks
   - c. water
   - d. flowers

3. Do you want to be a writer? Many people have this dream. They take courses about how to write. If you want to be a writer, you should also read a lot. If you read a lot, you can learn how _____.
   - a. other people write
   - b. many people dream
   - c. other people read
   - d. some people work

4. Scientists say that music is good for you. It can be classical or jazz or pop—any kind of music. When you are sad, it can help you feel happier. When you are sick, it can help you _____.
   - a. feel younger
   - b. play music
   - c. get well
   - d. hear better

5. Malaria is a terrible disease. About 5 million people get it every year. About 1 million people die from it. Many of them are children in poor families. They don't eat enough food, so they are _____.
   - a. bad students
   - b. small and weak
   - c. never at home
   - d. big and strong

6. There's lots of interesting artwork in museums in New York. But some museums are also works of art. One of these is the Guggenheim Museum. People go there to see the paintings and photographs, and also to see the _____.
   - a. artwork
   - b. other people
   - c. street
   - d. building

ANSWER KEY

PART 2

UNIT 1

Test 1 *(page 5)*

1. adverb
2. adjective, noun
3. noun
4. noun
5. noun
6. noun
7. adjective, verb
8. verb

Test 2 *(page 6)*

1. verb; to say that something is true, although you would prefer not to say it
2. verb; to begin using a new way of doing something
3. verb; to become a student at a college or school
4. verb; to become the legal parents of a child that is not your own child
5. noun; the price you pay to go to a movie, museum, sports event, etc.
6. verb; to allow someone to enter a place

Test 3 *(page 7)*

1. lose her balance, was off balance, strike a balance
2. a plate, on one foot, her children's needs
3. off balance, on balance
4. balanced diet
5. go bald

Test 4 *(page 8)*

1. a. surface
   b. rate
   c. amounts
   d. numbers
   e. temperature
2. a. We'll be even.
   b. The first half of the game was very even.
3. Spread … evenly
4. a. even out
   b. even up
5. a. even out the difference
   b. even up the score

UNIT 2

Tests 1 & 2 *(pages 9–12)*

Answers will vary.

Test 3 *(page 13)*

Answers will vary.

UNIT 3

(The words given in these answers are from the 100 Words list. Other words that fit correctly into the spaces are acceptable.)

Test 1 *(page 14)*

A.

1. said	13. know
2. would	14. way
3. other	15. work
4. down	16. use
5. them	17. because
6. there	18. most
7. this	19. took
8. been	20. thought
9. after	21. which
10. first	22. think
11. into	23. only
12. people	24. could

B.

1. What	9. you
2. here	10. for
3. at	11. with
4. are	12. of
5. there	13. this
6. in	14. come
7. about	15. your
8. like	16. time

Test 2 *(page 15)*

(The words listed here are from the 100 Words list. Any other words are also acceptable.)

much, who, other, and, have, is, me, has, in, we, one, do, its, could, more, made, this, to, even, would, with, then, had, one, did, into, no, her, new, went, the, say

Test 3 *(page 16)*

A.

1. some	16. good
2. there	17. gives
3. was	18. down
4. have	19. thought
5. just	20. have
6. After	21. looked
7. for	22. that
8. back	23. your
9. said	24. day
10. get	25. my
11. day	26. all
12. two	27. takes
13. more	28. you
14. Are	29. want
15. here	30. even

B.

Answers will vary.

UNIT 4

Test 1 *(page 18)*

1. grandchildren/grandsons/granddaughters
2. live
3. housework/shopping/cooking/cleaning
4. In
5. far
6. people

Test 2 *(page 19)*

1. country
2. school
3. ride
4. fast/quickly
5. car/truck
6. ends/finishes

Test 3 *(page 20)*

1. Part of speech: adjective; General meaning: not mixed with anything else
2. Part of speech: noun; General meaning: a loud sound made by a lion
3. Part of speech: noun; General meaning: the people watching a movie
4. Part of speech: adverbial phrase; General meaning: without help from anyone
5. Part of speech: verb; General meaning: to say something very quietly
6. Part of speech: adjective; General meaning: not nice to look at, not beautiful

Test 4 *(page 21)*

1. Part of speech: adjective; General meaning: worth a lot of money
2. Part of speech: noun; General meaning: small case (thing) that holds your money or plastic cards
3. Part of speech: verb; General meaning: stop going to school
4. Part of speech: noun; General meaning: small piece of paper or cloth attached to something with information on it
5. Part of speech: verb; General meaning: to shout to show support for someone or something
6. Part of speech: adverbial phrase; General meaning: many times but not all the time

UNIT 5

Test 1 *(page 22)*

1. Root: afraid
   Prefix: un-
   Meaning of prefix: not
   Meaning of word: not afraid
2. Root: violent
   Prefix: non-
   Meaning of prefix: not
   Meaning of word: not violent
3. Root: historic (history)
   Prefix: pre-
   Meaning of prefix: before
   Meaning of word: before history
4. Root: continue
   Prefix: dis-
   Meaning of prefix: not
   Meaning of word: not continue
5. Root: use
   Prefix: mis-
   Meaning of prefix: badly
   Meaning of word: use badly
6. Root: ground
   Prefix: under-
   Meaning of prefix: under (below)
   Meaning of word: below the ground
7. Root: sense
   Prefix: non-
   Meaning of prefix: not
   Meaning of word: without sense or meaning
8. Root: health
   Prefix: un-
   Meaning of prefix: not
   Meaning of word: not good for your health

Test 2 (*page 23*)

1. Root: dirty (dirt)
   Part of speech of root: adjective (noun)
   Suffix: -est
   Part of speech of root + suffix: adjective in superlative form
   Meaning of word: the most dirty
2. Root: dark
   Part of speech of root: adjective, noun
   Suffix: -ness
   Part of speech of root + suffix: noun
   Meaning of word: when there is no light
3. Root: drive
   Part of speech of root: verb
   Suffix: -er
   Part of speech of root + suffix: noun
   Meaning of word: a person who drives
4. Root: help
   Part of speech of root: verb, noun
   Suffix: -less
   Part of speech of root + suffix: adjective
   Meaning of word: not able to take care of yourself
5. Root: use
   Part of speech of root: noun, verb
   Suffix: -ful
   Part of speech of root + suffix: adjective
   Meaning of word: helping you to do or get what you want
6. Root: warm
   Part of speech of root: adjective
   Suffix: -er
   Part of speech of root + suffix: adjective in the comparative form
   Meaning of word: more warm
7. Root: close
   Part of speech of root: adjective, verb
   Suffix: -ly
   Part of speech of root + suffix: adverb
   Meaning of word: from nearby, very carefully
8. Root: care
   Part of speech of root: noun, verb
   Suffix: -less
   Part of speech of root + suffix: adjective
   Meaning of word: without care or attention

Test 3 (*page 24*)

	Noun	Verb	Adjective	Adverb
1.	stranger	X	strange	strangely
2.	sadness	sadden	sad	sadly
3.	sleep	sleep	sleepy	sleepily
4.	openness	open	open	openly
5.	darkness	darken	dark	darkly
6.	help	help	helpless, helpful	helplessly helpfully

Test 4 (*page 25*)

	Noun	Verb	Adjective	Adverb
1.	anger	anger	angry	angrily
2.	sweetness	sweeten	sweet	sweetly
3.	loudness	X	loud	loudly
4.	reality	realize	real	really
5.	direction, director	direct	direct	directly
6.	freedom	free	free	freely

UNIT 6

Test 1 (*page 26*)

1. put on
2. got off
3. turn off
4. get out
5. wait for
6. look up
7. fell down
8. get up
9. take off
10. lie down

Test 2 (*page 27*)

1. at first
2. right away
3. all the time
4. At last
5. all day long
6. on time
7. After a while
8. for now

Test 3 (*page 28*)

1. in the middle of
2. on top of
3. in back of
4. next to
5. in front of
6. On the right

Test 4 (page 29)

1. <u>Ho Kwangliang</u> <u>lives</u> in Taichung, Taiwan.
      S   V

2. <u>He</u> <u>is</u> the president of Hung Ming Enterprises.
    S V

3. <u>His company</u> <u>makes</u> parts of shoes.
      S   V

4. <u>Many shoe companies</u> <u>buy</u> from Ho's company.
          S   V

5. <u>He</u> <u>does</u> business with famous companies in the
    S   V
   United States and Europe.

6. <u>Hung Ming Enterprises</u> <u>makes</u> $25 million every
         S   V
   year.

7. There <u>are</u> <u>four buildings</u> with lots of machines.
        V   S

8. <u>One hundred people</u> <u>work</u> in them.
        S   V

9. <u>Ho</u> <u>plans</u> to open a new company in Shanghai,
    S   V
   China.

10. <u>That company</u> <u>will make</u> shoelaces.
       S   V

11. At first, <u>Ho</u> <u>will work</u> in Shanghai.
           S   V

12. Then <u>his son</u> <u>will take</u> his place.
         S   V

Test 5 (page 30)

1. <u>Maya</u> <u>has</u> a job at a clothing company in
    S   V
   Ecuador.

2. <u>The company</u> <u>sells</u> clothes to stores in the
      S   V
   United States.

3. <u>Maya</u> <u>works</u> on the company's website.
    S   V

4. <u>Many people in the company</u> <u>use</u> the website.
          S   V

5. <u>People outside the company</u> <u>use</u> the website,
          S   V
   too.

6. <u>They</u> <u>look</u> at the website to see the clothes.
    S   V

7. <u>Maya's work</u> <u>is</u> important to the company.
      S   V

8. Sometimes there <u>are</u> <u>problems</u> with the website.
            V   S

9. <u>She</u> <u>works</u> hard and <u>fixes</u> the problems quickly.
    S   V   V

10. Sometimes <u>she</u> <u>stays</u> late.
            S   V

11. <u>Maya's job</u> <u>is</u> not easy.
       S   V

12. But <u>it's</u> important to her and to the company.
       S V

Test 6 (page 31)

1. They
2. They
3. he
4. Their
5. they
6. they
7. They
8. it
9. They
10. her
11. he
12. He
13. He
14. he
15. he
16. They
17. him
18. they

Test 7 (page 33)

1. She bought the sofa from Sharon, <u>who</u> is moving to California.
   She bought the sofa from Sharon. Sharon is moving to California.

2. We stayed at a hotel <u>that</u> my brother stays at often.
   We stayed at a hotel. My brother often stays at the hotel.

3. Marie got an A on the chemistry exam, <u>which</u> was the most difficult one.
   Marie got an A on the chemistry exam. The chemistry exam was the most difficult one.

4. Today I finally got the letter <u>that</u> I was waiting for.
   Today I finally got the letter. I was waiting for the letter.

5. Maurice only likes bananas <u>that</u> are still green.
   Maurice only likes bananas. The bananas are still green.

6. Zita opened the new computer <u>that</u> she bought in New York.
   Zita opened the new computer. She bought the new computer in New York.

7. The night was very cold, <u>which</u> was not good for the plants.
   The night was very cold. The cold was not good for the plants.

8. Brian started talking to an old man <u>who</u> was sitting next to him.
   Brian started talking to an old man. The old man was sitting next to him.

Test 8 *(page 34)*

1. Lang is going to the show that starts at 10:00.
2. He went to talk to the professor who is teaching the course.
3. Lisa lives in a nice part of Paris that is full of good shops and restaurants.
4. My friend and I visited Bulgaria, which is a very beautiful country.
5. We often listen to that singer, who died last year.
6. We didn't enjoy the weather, which was very hot.
7. Walter only buys meat that comes from farms near here.
8. Today we finally met the young people who live next door.

PART 3
UNIT 1

Tests 1, 2, 4–7 *(pages 37, 38, 40–43)*. These can be self-corrected by students.

Test 3 *(page 39)*

1. woke	10. hour
2. eat	11. been
3. war	12. wear
4. late	13. date
5. soon	14. do
6. paid	15. mile
7. speak	16. say
8. lie	17. seen
9. what	18. say

Test 8 *(page 44)*
Focus on Vocabulary

1. b	6. a
2. c	7. c
3. a	8. a
4. c	9. b
5. b	

Test 9 *(page 45)*
Focus on Vocabulary

1. funny
2. violent
3. trouble
4. tax
5. popular
6. smart
7. successful
8. interested
9. earn

UNIT 2

Test 1 *(page 46)*

1. Bernard Dadié
2. Work
3. Nathalie Sarraute
4. "The Doll Queen"
5. two
6. page 65
7. four
8. Argentina

Test 2 *(page 48)*

1. traditional jazz, Broadway, or pop songs
2. 7:00 P.M. to 8:30 P.M.
3. Villas
4. Tuesdays
5. access to a piano
6. comfortable clothing and gym shoes
7. Beginner to Intermediate
8. Latin dances

Test 3 *(page 50)*

1. 1978
2. more than $6 million
3. Stanford University
4. They were professional tennis players.
5. at least until 2012
6. 1998
7. Australian Open, French Open, U.S. Open, Wimbledon
8. when they were four

Test 4 *(page 52)*
Focus on Vocabulary

1. c	6. a
2. a	7. b
3. b	8. a
4. b	9. c
5. a	10. b

Test 5 *(page 53)*
Focus on Vocabulary

1. career
2. careful
3. prize
4. Naturally
5. several
6. continued
7. relatives
8. jokes
9. teenage
10. private

UNIT 3

Test 1 (page 54)
1. hat
2. raincoat
3. skirt
4. pants
5. shoes

Test 2 (page 55)
1. walls
2. floor
3. table
4. clock
5. computer

Test 3 (page 56)
1. in the kitchen
2. mother/father and son/daughter, or wife and husband
3. the dinner he/she is cooking
4. B is not happy about the dinner, and A is not happy about what B says because he/she complains (says bad things) about his/her cooking.

Test 4 (page 57)
1. on the phone, at home, or together somewhere (not at school)
2. two students in high school
3. the interview A had for a job or for a college
4. A thinks the interview went badly and he/she might not get the job or get into the college. B is sure that A will get the job or get into the college.

Test 5 (page 58)
1. in Mr. Shattuck's/Robert's house
2. two women, one who works in Mr. Shattuck's house
3. Robert and Lila
4. She leaves a ring that Robert gave to her. She has probably decided not to marry him.

Test 6 (page 59)
1. in a classroom
2. a boy named Jack and someone else, probably another student
3. the teacher
4. a test

Test 7 (page 60)
Focus on Vocabulary
1. c
2. b
3. a
4. b
5. a
6. c
7. b
8. a
9. c
10. a

Test 8 (page 61)
Focus on Vocabulary
1. record
2. missed
3. decided
4. moment
5. compete
6. distance
7. mistake
8. adults
9. weak
10. training

UNIT 4

Test 1 (page 62)
1. countries in South America
2. sciences (science subjects)
3. electronics (electronic entertainment equipment)
4. parts of a house or building
5. dairy products (things made from milk)
6. people who write
7. personal pronouns
8. names of women
9. car makers
10. things in a bathroom

Test 2 (page 63)
1. cities in Canada
2. American units of measurement (ways of measuring)
3. long rivers
4. outdoor clothing for cold weather
5. places in an airport
6. kinds of housework
7. kinds of programs on TV
8. seas
9. places in a hotel
10. ways of describing land

Test 3 (page 64)

(Answers may vary.)
 1. period; punctuation
 2. chairs; restaurant
 3. president; leaders of countries
 4. towels; things at a beach
 5. thirty-three; multiples of eleven
 6. gym; places at a school or college
 7. make-up artist; people and things for making a movie
 8. Lincoln; American presidents
 9. dog; pets
10. road; where cars drive

Test 4 (page 65)

 1. (Morocco) countries that are islands
 2. (Sun) planets
 3. (doors) parts of a bicycle
 4. (cube) two-dimensional shapes/(circle) shapes with straight lines
 5. (window) things you put on a wall
 6. (hairdryer) electric appliances usually in the kitchen
 7. (nest) parts of a plane
 8. (table) things and people at a basketball game
 9. (snow skiing) water sports
10. (fish) ingredients for a cake/foods that go into a cake

Test 5 (page 66)
Focus on Vocabulary

1. b	6. a
2. a	7. c
3. c	8. b
4. a	9. c
5. b	10. c

Test 6 (page 67)
Focus on Vocabulary

 1. accident
 2. outside
 3. take care of
 4. notice
 5. cousin(s)
 6. headache
 7. camp
 8. renting
 9. amount
10. invited

UNIT 5
Test 1 (page 68)

 1. Not a paragraph
 2. Paragraph
 3. Paragraph
 4. Not a paragraph

Test 2 (page 69)

 1. b
 2. a
 3. c

Test 3 (page 70)

 1. Adventure travel vacations
 2. Cooking vacations
 3. Animal-watching vacations

Test 4 (page 71)

 1. Comfortable workplace chairs
 2. The dining table
 3. People and their furniture

Test 5 (page 72)

 1. Sentence: b
    Topic: The Maori people in New Zealand
 2. Sentence: a
    Topic: The *haka* dance
 3. Sentence: c
    Topic: New Zealand in the movies

Test 6 (page 73)

A.

1. b	6. b
2. a	7. a
3. a	8. b
4. b	9. a
5. a	10. b

B.

 1. The job of a bus driver is not easy in the city.
    In the morning and the evening, the buses are often stopped in traffic.
    People on the buses get angry because they move slowly.
    Bus drivers hate the traffic, too.
    They have to watch the road carefully all the time.
    They have to be ready to stop quickly.

2. Police officers have many kinds of jobs in the
city.
Some of them are traffic police.
They try to help the traffic move through the
city.
Other police officers work to stop crime.
They try to stop bad people from breaking into
homes or stores.
They also try to stop bad people from hurting
others.

Test 7 *(page 74)*

1. Extra sentence: Some dogs have funny names.
Topic: Cats: better pets than dogs
2. Extra sentence: A house with a large yard is
expensive.
Topic: The right pet for you
3. Extra sentence: Dogs usually don't like cats.
Topic: Dogs: good company for people

Test 8 *(page 75)*
Focus on Vocabulary

1. a
2. c
3. b
4. b
5. c
6. a
7. c
8. b
9. c
10. a

Test 9 *(page 76)*
Focus on Vocabulary

1. actress
2. partner
3. energy
4. peace
5. really
6. recognized
7. dream
8. able
9. grew
10. director

PART 4
UNIT 1

Test 1 *(page 78)*

1. d
2. c
3. c

4. b
5. a
6. b

Test 2 *(page 79)*

1. b
2. a
3. d
4. c
5. a
6. a

UNIT 2

Test 1 *(page 80)*

1. c
2. a
3. d
4. a
5. d
6. b

Test 2 *(page 81)*

1. a
2. d
3. c
4. b
5. d
6. c

UNIT 3

Test 1 *(page 82)*

1. d
2. a
3. b
4. c
5. b
6. a

Test 2 *(page 83)*

1. b
2. d
3. a
4. c
5. b
6. d